The Healing Powers
of Nature

The Healing Powers
of Nature

A Fascinating Guide to the Traditional
Use of 200 Medicinal Herbs

Antonin Příhoda

HAMLYN

Publisher's note

This book contains information on a wide range of plants that are, or can be used in the treatment of human disorders. It is primarily intended to be read as a source of interesting information and not as a practical guide to self-medication.
It cannot be over-emphasised that many herbs are poisonous, some extremely so, and some which are beneficial in small doses can also be harmful if taken to excess or for long periods. The advice of a qualified medical or herbal practitioner should always be sought before using herbal remedies.
It is recommended that all herbal infusions and decoctions should be freshly prepared and should certainly be used within twelve hours of making up.
We should like to stress that the use of any plant or derivative is entirely at the reader's own risk and we hereby disclaim all legal responsibility for any harmful or unwanted effects that might arise from such use.

Illustrated by
L. Urban and V. Ničová
Translated by Clare Krojzlová
Graphic design Miloš Lang
English version first published in 1989
by the Hamlyn Publishing Group,
a division of the Octopus Publishing Group,
Michelin House, 81 Fulham Road,
London SW3 6RB

© 1989 Artia, Prague

ISBN 0 600 56715 X

Printed in Czechoslovakia by TSNP Martin
3/21/01/51-01

Contents

Medicinal plants yesterday and today

For centuries, indeed for thousands of years, people have looked to herbs for help, or at least relief, in illness and in a wide variety of health problems. Both good and bad information and advice have been handed down from generation to generation, and from time immemorial attempts have also been made to formalize these in writing. Groundless superstition was often mixed with actual experience with medicinal plants, for people sensed mysterious forces in the way herbs could overcome disease and so attributed magical powers to them. Their medicinal action was often associated with religious rites and magical incantations. However, we should not wholly dismiss the psychotherapeutic significance of this: even today, with all the progress in modern medicine, the persuasive words of the doctor frequently play an important role. Similarly, we also know of cases of less than responsible modern herbalists who are able to influence their customers psychologically with clever propaganda.

At first, popular healing developed separately in different parts of the world. Long before scientific research into the foxglove, the beneficial effects, in some cases, of this poisonous plant on the activity of the heart were known in Europe, while Central American Indians used the flowers of some cacti for the same purpose. An extract made from Biting Stonecrop (*Sedum acre*) was once used in Europe for rinsing ulcerated gums and was taken for scurvy. An identical method of treatment for scurvy and diseased gums was used by the Mexican Indians, who crushed the leaves of the American stonecrop *Sedum dendroideum*. For cosmetic purposes, ointments and lotions made from Biting Stonecrop were used in France to redden the face and lips, while Mexican Indians prepared an extract made from the blossoms of the cactus *Aporocactus flagelliformis* for the same purpose.

Many theories on the use of medicinal plants arose because people recognized similarities in shape between parts of plants and organs of the human body. It was presumed that particular plants had medicinal effects on diseases of these organs simply because of this superficial similarity.

With increasing knowledge of the healing properties of plants came an awareness of plant poisons and narcotics. People learned to use them, for example, to help when hunting fish and game, but also to misuse them against members of their own tribes, society and even families. This knowledge was exploited in antiquity, the Middle Ages and the Renaissance in the misused art of poisoning. In modern times the effects of this knowledge are seen in drug addiction and drug-induced diseases. It is, therefore, both difficult and important to select and verify scientifically those plants, known from folk tradition and ancient herbaria, which are truly beneficial and useful.

The use of plants in popular healing, as well as in the production of dyes, implements and adornments, and in religious rites and folk customs, is the subject of a special branch of knowledge known as ethnobotany. The ways that different peoples have used plants have been researched and books about the verified medical use of plants, drawing from folk tradition, have been written. One aspect of ethnobotany is pharmacoethnography, that is the study of remedies and drugs. In recent years this science has been directing its attention mainly to tropical regions. Scientific expeditions identify and research drugs used by peoples still living in close contact with nature in areas that are relatively untouched by civilization. Equally, the ancient records of peoples with thousands of years of culture behind them, particularly Asian societies, are a further valuable source of information. The ethnobotany of European peoples, however, also contains a wealth of knowledge on which modern scientific research can draw. In Romania, for example, extracts and decoctions of various medicinal plants were – and in places still are – used preventively when bathing small children. In Poland breast-feeding mothers drink decoctions of medicinal plants, the active constituents of which pass into the mothers' milk to provide protection against disease or even to treat it in their babies. This action has now been medically verified and is recommended by the official Polish prescription list. In the USSR, the application of medicinal plants in the treatment of fatal tumours is being examined scientifically, and there is some evidence that they are effective, particularly in the case of tumours of the alimentary canal and the epidermis.

Research during the preparation of this book has drawn on literary sources on medicinal plants, as well as traditional uses in France, Spain, Switzerland, Italy, Yugoslavia, Romania, Hungary, Czechoslovakia, Poland, Germany, the Soviet Union, America and Mexico.

Modern science is gradually explaining superstition and removing errors from popular healing. At the same time, chemical analysis and biological study are frequently confirming things which were formerly known only from experience and which had no rational explanation. Natural antibiotics effective against bacteria, viruses and certain fungi were discovered relatively recently for instance, but people have used plants containing these substances since the earliest times. It is sometimes even possible to substantiate what appears to be pure superstition and confirm the validity of advice handed down by tradition. Old prescription lists, for example, recom-

mended the collecting of medicinal plants before the feast of St John the Baptist (24 June). This is the time when many plants begin to flower and when intensive chemical transformations take place. Therefore, they contain the maximum quantities of active constituents in midsummer. Scientific knowledge about medicinal plants is increasing all the time. However, many plants used in popular healing all over the world have been noted, but have not yet been fully researched.

It is beyond doubt that plant drugs are a valuable source of raw materials for the production of medicines. Using plant drugs, according to a doctor's prescription, is equally of undisputed importance. However, bringing popular healing to a wider public is always a difficult task. There are still many people who prefer to trust their own judgement rather than that of a doctor, but only a doctor is competent to diagnose an illness correctly and to prescribe the method of treatment. Consequently, most books on medicinal plants avoid giving specific instructions on how to use the plants. On the other hand, if people do not find instructions in modern books they will look for them in old herbaria laden with superstition, recommend garbled recipes to each other, or consult herbalists who may not always be competent or qualified.

Having said that treatment should be restricted exclusively to trained practitioners does not mean that home treatment with medicinal plants should be rejected completely. Their use in the home lies chiefly in the prevention of disease, dealing with common health problems, such as sore throats, coughs, mild inflammation and minor digestive problems, and in bathing chronic limb complaints. They are also useful as dietary and cosmetic remedies. Drinking diuretic teas, with a doctor's approval, can have a beneficial effect for sufferers from kidney stones, and a regular intake of diabetic tea is recommended for milder forms of diabetes. Plants rich in vitamins and natural antibiotics can often protect during influenza epidemics against falling ill, or at least reduce the seriousness of the infection.

Using appropriate medicinal herbs, without harmful side-effects, can give an additional feeling of complete health and mental well-being. Suitably selected medicinal plants taken in moderate doses are a source of vitamins and other beneficial substances which people often lack in their normal and often monotonous diet. It can certainly do no harm for a person, at least occasionally, to alternate ordinary coffee or tea with a decoction or extract made from medicinal plants. This book is intended to help the reader to identify and use correctly many medicinal plants. It gives warnings about poisonous plants and recommends the preparation of simple home remedies — teas, decoctions, compresses, baths and so on.

Animals and medicinal plants

E. Thompson-Seton, in his book *Wild Animals' Ways*, describes how a bear digs in the ground, chews and gulps down peppery plant roots, one after the other, white tubers which sting and scratch his throat, constrict the intestines and burn like hot ashes. However, he keeps digging on and on, chewing the plant roots while moaning and whimpering. We assume that a bear, which eats only a meat diet, is often attacked by a terrible disease, which mainly infects the skin. This disease occurs most often in those which regularly eat only wild boar. Pain manifests itself in a burning and itching of the skin and it is as if the whole body were being burned by billions of little flames. We are not quite sure, but we assume that peppery roots provide the animal with relief — albeit small — but the pain nevertheless subsides.

Under certain circumstances, animals will seek out medicinal (even highly poisonous) plants. In the Boreč National Reserve situated in the Central Bohemian Highlands a doe was observed throughout a whole evening searching for Valerian plants of the genus Sambucifolia. She kept on climbing after these, even over stony debris and inaccessible rocks, although there was ample and richer pasture near her. In Tatranska Lomnica, in the High Tatras, some stags and their does used to go into a garden at night and graze on plants in the rockery, including poisonous monkshoods (Aconitum), probably in order to get rid of parasites. In the conservation area of the White Carpathians in Moravia, the original meadows and pastures have been stripped of trees and bushes, ploughed over and sown with a mixture of shamrock grasses. These, according to chemical analysis, should provide the richest nutrition, but beef cattle raised on pastures treated in this way began to suffer from parasitic worms. They often broke through their simple enclosures and ran off *en masse* to the Slovak side of the White Carpathians, where natural meadows remained with their original, much richer flora. There they would seek out particular plants, many of which were poisonous. When myxomatosis, a disease fatal to rabbits, penetrated Czechoslovakia, wild rabbits went into graveyards, gardens and parks in droves, where they grazed on poisonous woody plants of the genera Thuja, Platycladus, Chamaecyparis, Juniperus and Taxus, which they would previously have ignored. Rabbits with access to these plants survived, whereas elsewhere they died out completely.

Sheep breeders in Slovakia noticed that,

occasionally, rams, and sometimes also ewes, would crush tufts of Tansy (*Tanacetum vulgare*) with their heads. Normally, they avoid this plant when grazing. The sheep breeders attempted to explain this by suggesting that the animals were deliberately destroying plants which, when consumed in the absence of other adequate grazing, are said to cause ewes to abort. The true explanation is, in fact, much simpler. The aromatic constituents evaporating from the sap of the Tansy repel insects and sheep crush the Tansy during the period when they are most troubled by flies. Consequently, at certain times of the year, they can protect the most vulnerable parts of their heads from flies. Fishermen also sometimes rub their faces, necks and hands with crushed Tansy leaves to protect themselves from mosquitoes, a method which can be effective for an average of 20–30 minutes. *Artemisia annua* has a similar and even stronger effect.

An article appeared in the press suggesting that chimpanzees living in the wild know and use plant remedies. This was prompted by the results of research carried out by scientists from the universities of Michigan and California. Chimpanzees in Tanzania, for example, like to seek out the leaves of a plant of the genus Aspilia which contain the antibiotic thiarubin-A. This antibiotic destroys the bacteria which cause several diseases.

Medicinal plants in pharmacology

The basis for the reliable use of medicinal plants in pharmacology consists mainly of chemical analysis. This is often very complex and exacting. In addition, biological tests of isolated constituents are made on animals, cell cultures, experimental cultures of bacteria, fungi and so on. The drug (i.e. usually the dried, crude plant used to prepare remedies or for the extraction of important substances of plant origin) may be given directly or in the form of a simple preparation as a remedy, or after processing in pharmaceutical laboratories and factories.

In the past, drugs were usually processed in small quantities and made into various tinctures, ointments, extracts, etc. in individual pharmacies. Nowadays, the active constituents are isolated first. In spite of constant development in the manufacture of synthetic medicines, drugs of plant origin are still widely used. Drugs permitted for retail sale or which are available on prescription are listed in the pharmacopoeias of individual countries. These pharmacopoeias contain the criteria for drug quality and also give methods of verifying this quality.

The collection of medicinal plants

The main principle is that medicinal plants should not be collected during damp or rainy weather or when they are wet with dew. The main section of the book gives details of the most suitable time for collection and which parts of individual plants are required, listed under each species. It is important that the plants are handled carefully and not damaged. For example, breaking off the leaves can adversely affect the active constituents and contact with metal can destroy vitamin C and tannins. As far as possible, plants and parts of plants should be collected whole and cut up with scissors or a knife only after drying.

These days, we encounter difficulties in collecting medicinal plants which herbalists did not have in the past. A polluted environment − dust, smoke and ashes − has an undesirable effect on growing plants. The most serious damage to plants may be caused by the incorrect use of chemical pesticides and weedkillers. These are usually poisonous or very damaging to human health. Plants treated with these chemicals and weeds on to which they have been transported by the wind are dangerous. Plants may also frequently be unhygienic and unhealthy to use because they have been sprinkled or flooded with impure or polluted water or because the meadow or field in which they are growing has been manured with farmyard or other manure or polluted directly by people and animals. Therefore, plants should not be gathered from roadsides, in villages, close to railway lines, from ditches with sewage water or from similar locations. Plants from such places may be dangerous to those who work with them later. A dirty and cloudy decoction of linden blossoms gathered from dusty town streets or from a factory yard where they are coated with tar substances is unlikely to promote health in the same way as a clear and honey-fragrant decoction of linden blossoms that have grown in a clean atmosphere. In some areas where there is permanent pollution from industrial effluent, gathering or cultivating medicinal plants is not recommended at all. When gathering in fields, meadows and woodland, take care that these wild plants have not recently been sprayed or otherwise polluted.

The drying and care of medicinal plants

Most plants are dried in the shade at a fixed maximum temperature. For plants containing volatile essential oils, the temperature should not exceed 40 °C (104 °F). Dry the plants in a place where they are in no danger of contamination from dust or animals. Dry each species separately so that they do not become mixed up or contaminated by fragments from other plants. The drying trays must be clean and, ideally, should be covered with wrapping paper. Use a fresh sheet of paper for each aromatic plant as it readily absorbs the fragrance. Do not add fresh or damp plants to plants that are already drying out or have finished drying, even if they are of the same species, because the drying plants then become moist again and moulds may grow.

When storing dried medicinal plants, protect them from damp and dust and from being attacked by insects. The active ingredients of some plants even need to be protected from light. The best containers are well-sealed tins, glass jars covered with cellophane or a similar material, paper or jute sacks and cardboard boxes lined with paper, depending on the quantity, species and properties of the drug. Plastic bags are not suitable, as even a slightly damp plant will go mouldy. Moreover, if they are used for plants containing essential oils, they can draw off the oils and so render the plant useless. Similarly, storage for long periods in canvas sacks is also unsuitable: canvas lets in dust and presents no obstacle to insects. The species should always be marked on the container, together with the date of collection. As drugs lose their efficacy with age, they are not normally stored for long.

The preparation of home medicines

In some cases, fresh plants may be processed or the sap pressed from them. Generally, however, dried medicinal plants are used and either a decoction is prepared or an extract is made with boiling or cold water. Sometimes an alcohol extract is more suitable. In this case, either fresh or dried plants are macerated in alcohol for a specific time. Jam can be made from the fruits. When the healing constituent of a plant is not volatile, it is possible to prepare a thickened decoction with sugar in the form of a syrup. The way to handle individual drugs is stated with the plant descriptions.

Dangers when using medicinal plants

Incorrect use of medicinal plants can seriously damage your health. Possible errors include wrong identification of a plant, ignorance of its properties and side-effects, incorrect dosage, unsuitable combinations of drugs (either other medicinal plant drus or proprietary or prescribed medicines) and treatment of incorrectly diagnosed illnesses. Use only plants that you know well and check their correct use with an expert. Old, contaminated, mixed or unmarked plants should be thrown away. Always discard mouldy plants as some moulds are poisonous. These are mainly fungi of the genus Stachybotrys. For example, the olive-grey to blackish-grey coatings on dry plants, hay, straw, paper and some fruits and seeds are carriers of the so-called farmers' disease. The whitish to pink mycelia of the microscopic fungi of the genus Fusarium sometimes grow on starch-containing parts of plants. Some of these produce poisons that cannot be destroyed even by boiling or baking. These poisons depress the formation of white blood cells, which are an essential part of the body's immune system. The microscopic fungi *Aspergillus flavus* and *Aspergillus oryzae* and some related species, which form yellow and greenish-yellow or brownish-yellow mouldy growths on fat- and starch-containing plant organs, are particularly dangerous. They produce highly poisonous substances called aflatoxins which damage the liver. Equally dangerous is the *Aspergillus ochraceus* fungus which causes yellow, brownish, orange to orange-red mouldy coatings on various parts of the plant.

Incorrect self-diagnosis can cause great harm. Even simply increasing the amount of a decoction, extract or tea can damage your health. For example, even a liquid prepared from an entirely harmless plant can exacerbate problems with kidney function and blood circulation. Never, therefore, interfere in the treatment of illnesses associated with high fever, sudden cramps or severe pain without consulting a doctor and do not use any preparations without his or her recommendation. Long-term illnesses should also be left to doctors. The frequent use of certain plant drugs, even if they improve the condition at first, can later aggravate an illness. It is, therefore, a good idea to interrupt treatment or alternate different drugs with similar effects. A regular intake of medicinal tea is helpful in the treatment of kidney stones, but even here it is a good idea to alternate the particular diuretic used with others from time to time.

Healing of one part of the body can place a burden on other parts. In addition, it may uncover a concealed disease or aggravate the effects of a previous illness. You should never use medicinal plants in the case of infectious jaundice or other liver diseases, for example, without consulting a doctor, nor should you treat yourself with medicinal plants when you are also taking prescribed medicines, as the former may interfere with the effects of the latter. It is especially important to bear in mind that drinking alcoholic extracts made from medicinal plants, a form of traditional, popular healing favoured by some people, can seriously reduce the effect of prescribed medicines or even cause them to be harmful simply because of the alcohol content.

Poisonous medicinal plants

Some medicinal plants are highly poisonous, not only when swallowed but because their poisons can be absorbed through the skin. These should never be used for home treatment. When handling certain species, gloves should be worn and the dust of the dried plant should not be inhaled. After collecting poisonous (and ideally all) plants, wash your hands thoroughly. Children should never be allowed to collect poisonous plants.

Some plants contain substances which make the skin more sensitive to the sun's radiation. If the skin is exposed to the sun after contact with these plants, severe burning can occur.

Some people are sensitive to particular constituents of certain plants. Touching the plant, inhaling plant particles, such as pollen or damaged hairs, or contact with the volatile substances given off by some plants, can trigger unpleasant allergies, such as hayfever, rashes, blisters, and dangerous cramps which may be accompanied by choking to the point of unconsciousness. The causes of these allergies are difficult to ascertain. The culprits are often only identified when similar distressing symptoms recur in the same circumstances or location.

Protection of medicinal plants

Some medicinal plants are so rare today that they are officially protected. Sometimes, collecting any part of them is prohibited, sometimes only the parts growing above the ground may be collected. In these cases, it is better to obtain the required drugs from cultivated plants. Similarly, plants may not be collected from protected areas such as national parks and nature reserves. We should still take care even when gathering commoner, unrestricted medicinal plants to avoid severely reducing their numbers or even destroying a site completely. Do not pull plants up by the roots unnecessarily, particularly if it is sufficient to collect only the parts growing above ground. Always leave at least one-third of the plants on the site so that they can mature and produce seed. It is quite enough to cut off only the youngest aerial parts or just the flowering parts of some plants. They will then produce young shoots again and yield their harvest two or even more times in a year. Even so, do not collect from all the plants. Leave some undamaged because when plants flower for a second time, the fruits may no longer be able to mature or they may bear only non-germinating seeds. Also, damaged plants succumb more easily to frost and other unfavourable conditions. Commercial companies that use medicinal plants cultivate them in sufficient quantities. When collecting medicinal plants in the wild, we should bear in mind that they represent part of the wealth of nature, which should be conserved for future generations as well.

Plates

Key to symbols used:

▲ — protected plants

☠ — poisonous plants

I—XII — month of collection

🌿 — haulm

✾ — flower

🌾 — inflorescence

🍃 — leaf

🧅 — root, tuber, bulb

🍒 — fruit

🍇 — seed

🍂 — bark

🌱 — rhizome

Achillea millefolium L.
Yarrow

Compositae

● Yarrow is a perennial herb 20–80 cm (8–31 in) tall. The stems grow from the creeping rhizome. They are unbranched, densely leafed, mostly felted, very occasionally nearly glabrous, and topped with a panicle of small flower heads. The leaves are alternate, felted when young and later may be hairy or almost glabrous. They are pinnate with two or three lobes, divided into short blades and pointed at the tip. The overall shape of the leaf is tapering. The bracts are oval in shape and yellowish-green with a light to dark brown border at the edges. There are two types of flowers. In the centre of the conical receptacle there are about 20 tubular, bisexual, pentamerous and regular disc-florets, ranging in colour from dirty white to yellow. Around the edge, there are five ligulate, pistillate, symmetrical ray-florets. These are tridentate at the edges and coloured white or pink. There are scales among the disc-florets. The fruits are elongated, flattened, silver grey achenes, which are glabrous at the tip. They have narrow wings at the edges.

● Yarrow grows abundantly on dry meadows and pastures, on roadsides, ridges and in well-lit places in deciduous woods from lowland to hillsides. Plants with only white flowers grow on calcium-rich soils, but pink-flowered yarrows may grow on acid soils. Plants growing on acid soils have more of the active constituent (azulene) than plants growing on calcium-rich soils.

Collect basal leaf rosettes in May and at the beginning of June before the plant starts to flower and dry them in the shade. Cut off the whole inflorescence between June and September, allow it to wither and then cut off the individual flower heads, with the stalks as short as possible. Cut away the whole haulm between June and September so that the flowering tops have a length of 20–25 cm (8–10 in). Dry them in small bundles in the shade or by means of artificial heat up to 35 °C (95 °F). The plant must not change colour nor lose its aroma. It has a somewhat bitter taste.

The drug is given in the form of an extract to treat biliousness and other digestive problems, and to stimulate the activity of the bladder. It also has an anti-spasmodic effect. It can be used externally to treat inflammatory skin conditions. When taken internally for prolonged periods, dizziness and other disorders, such as rashes, have been observed in sensitive individuals.

Extract from the dried haulm for internal use: Pour 500 ml (18 fl oz) boiling water over 5 g ($\frac{1}{5}$ oz) (1 tablespoon) dried haulm and leave to infuse for 20 minutes.

Extract for external use: Pour 500 ml (18 fl oz) boiling water over 10 g ($\frac{2}{5}$ oz) dried haulm and leave to infuse for 20 minutes.

Aconitum callibotryon F. Reichenb.
Mountain Aconite

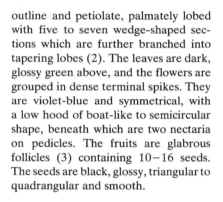

Ranunculaceae

● This perennial plant, which can grow up to 150 cm (59 in) in height, is highly poisonous. The greyish-brown turnip-shaped tubers (1) can grow up to 10 cm (4 in) long and 1–3 cm ($\frac{2}{5}$–1 in) wide. Branched, spindle-shaped roots grow out of the tubers. They are covered with fine, long, ramified root hairs. In the flowering season, apart from the main (mother) tuber, new (daughter) tubers with buds form. New plants grow from these in the following year. Not all of these flower, however. The stalks are erect and simple, branching only in the inflorescence. The leaves are alternate, circular in outline and petiolate, palmately lobed with five to seven wedge-shaped sections which are further branched into tapering lobes (2). The leaves are dark, glossy green above, and the flowers are grouped in dense terminal spikes. They are violet-blue and symmetrical, with a low hood of boat-like to semicircular shape, beneath which are two nectaria on pedicles. The fruits are glabrous follicles (3) containing 10–16 seeds. The seeds are black, glossy, triangular to quadrangular and smooth.

● Mountain Aconite grows in damp, mountainous and hilly regions, in forests, mainly along river valleys, by springs and so on. It is very variable and many other Aconite species resemble it. Hybrids are cultivated as ornamental plants in gardens. Wild Mountain Aconite is not used in popular healing because it is extremely poisonous.

Commercially prepared medicines are produced from cultivated plants. The beds should be laid out in damp, shady places. The seed is sown in autumn in rows 15 cm (6 in) apart, below the surface of the soil because it germinates only in darkness. The following year the seedlings are planted out. They require watering, weeding and hoeing two to three times a year. The tubers are not harvested until their fourth or fifth year. New plants may be started off from daughter tubers, in which case they can then be harvested as early as the October of the following year.

Only newly grown daughter tubers are used. The small roots are removed with a brush and bigger ones are cut in half. They are processed while fresh or dried in the shade by means of artificial heat at a temperature of 30–40 °C (86–104 °F). They need to be stored in dry, well-sealed tins and should not come into contact with other medicinal plants. In May and June the leaves may also be collected. These are either processed fresh or dried in the same way as the tubers.

Drugs for treating rheumatism and inflammation of the nerves are produced industrially from the dried plants.

Acorus calamus L.
Sweet Flag

Araceae

● This is a perennial herb that grows up to 150 cm (59 in) tall. It has a horizontal, creeping, ringed, fleshy, branched rhizome up to 50 cm (20 in) long and 3 cm (1 in) wide (1). The flowering stems (scapes) (2) and the leaves (3) grow out of the rhizome. The leaf-like scape is flat, triangular and reddish at the base. The spadix, which inclines to one side, grows from its upper part. A green sword-shaped spathe, which also resembles a leaf, grows in the same direction as the scape. The leaves are up to 1 m (39 in) long and 2 cm (5 in) wide. They are sword-shaped with undulated blades. They are joined to the rhizome by an enclosing, grooved sheath. The cone-shaped spadix is up to 8 cm (3 in) long and positioned close to the stalk. It is green to yellowish-green in colour and later turns brown. Individual tiny, densely clustered flowers are arranged spirally. They are bisexual, regular and have six greenish-yellow petals arranged in two whorls, six stamens and a pistil (4). The fruits do not mature in northern Europe and the plant reproduces only vegetatively.

● Sweet Flag is native to China and the Near East, where it was used as a spice and a medicine in ancient times. It grows in the mud of slow-flowing or still waters, on river banks around ponds and pools, in damp ditches and on marshes. It blossoms in June and July. It was first cultivated in Europe as early as the end of the 16th century, and has gradually become entirely naturalized.

The rhizomes of two- and three-year-old plants are collected between March and November. The most suitable time for gathering is in the autumn when ponds are drained. Large quantities of rhizomes can be picked out of the mud using special forks. The rhizomes are stripped of leaves and roots, rinsed thoroughly and cut into pieces. When they are required for special purposes, such as in the manufacture of confectionery, they are also peeled. Drying is not easy because of the very high water content in the rhizome and because of the smell it gives off. The rhizomes are dried by artificial heat at a temperature of 40 °C (104 °F) in places where there are no other medicinal plants. Correctly dried rhizomes are fragile and retain a pronounced spicy smell. This smell is even picked up by the drying shelves and containers, which cannot, therefore, subsequently be used for other plants.

Decoctions for improving digestion and for stimulating the appetite can be prepared from the unpeeled rhizome. Peeled rhizomes are used for making confectionery, which has similar but less pronounced effects.

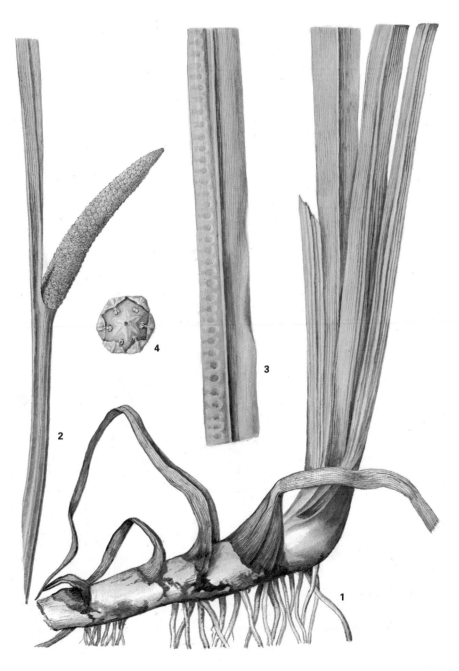

Adonis vernalis L.
Yellow Pheasant's Eye

 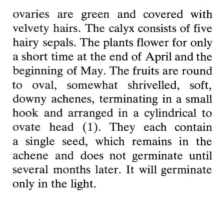

Ranunculaceae

● Yellow Pheasant's Eye is a poisonous perennial herb which grows from a short blackish-brown rhizome covered with long frayed fibres. Only some of the tall stalks flower. They are glabrous, covered with scales on the lower parts and densely leafed in the upper parts.

The leaves are alternate, glabrous or slightly downy and finely divided into a multitude of feathery entire lobes. The lemon yellow flower, 3–7 cm (1–3 in) in diameter, has up to 20 glossy, 2–3 cm ($\frac{3}{4}$–1 in) long petals and a large number of stamens and pistils. The ovaries are green and covered with velvety hairs. The calyx consists of five hairy sepals. The plants flower for only a short time at the end of April and the beginning of May. The fruits are round to oval, somewhat shrivelled, soft, downy achenes, terminating in a small hook and arranged in a cylindrical to ovate head (1). They each contain a single seed, which remains in the achene and does not germinate until several months later. It will germinate only in the light.

● Yellow Pheasant's Eye grows on dry, warm hillsides, rocky slopes or woodland plains with a sparse cover of deciduous trees and shrubs. It is often cultivated as an ornamental plant in gardens. It is a protected species in the wild, so only cultivated plants should be collected. Plant in a warm location in dry, light soil with a sufficient calcium content. Sow the achenes on the surface of the soil from June to October. Either sow directly in a well-prepared bed or in boxes and plant out the seedlings in spring. Although the plants will tolerate dry conditions, they need to be watered to produce a good crop. They also require weeding and hoeing.

Collect the entire haulm when it is in flower, without damaging the ground-level buds, from which new plants will grow the following year. It is best to cut off the plant a few centimetres above the ground. Remove the lower scaly parts of the stems without leaves and dry the haulms immediately in a well-ventilated place at a temperature of up to 50 °C (122 °F). The haulms should be laid out in thin layers to dry and turned carefully. It is more work to dry them suspended in bundles but this method produces a better result and the dried haulms are easier to wrap and do not get crushed. Store them in well-sealed containers to protect against damp.

Proprietary medicines for stimulating heart activity in elderly people are produced from this plant. It also has tranquillizing and mildly diuretic properties. As it is highly poisonous, it should never be used for home treatment.

1

20

Aegopodium podagraria L.
Ground Elder, Gout Weed

Umbelliferae

● Ground Elder is a perennial plant with stems that grow to a height of up to 100 cm (39 in). It forms an abundance of creeping rhizomes. These produce two to three times pinnately divided basal leaves borne on long, grooved, pale green petioles. The leaflets are tapering and pointed, with coarsely toothed edges. The stems are erect, branched and hollow, with angular grooves, and bear opposite, mainly trefoil leaves (3) with the petiole broadened below into a sheath. The leaflets are narrower than in the basal leaves and are often asymmetrical. The topmost leaves are entire. Flowers are in compound, terminal umbels composed of 10−20 umbellets and borne on coarsely hairy stems. They open from May to September and are white or slightly pink, some of them having only pistils (1), others being bisexual (2). The petals have cordate indentations. The fruits are elongated ovate achenes, flattened at the sides. They are light to dark brown when ripe and have straw-coloured grooves.

● Ground Elder grows on both lowlands and hillsides. It is usually abundant in damp and shady hedgerows, in orchards, open woodland, the damper spots of shady clearings and the edges of woods and along brooks and rivers.

The leaves and fruits have medicinal properties. They are dried in thin layers in the shade or in artificial heat up to a temperature of 30 °C (86 °F). Fresh leaves can also be used. Ground Elder is only important in popular healing. The young leaves are rich in vitamin C and may be prepared as a salad, served as a hot vegetable, rather like spinach, and added to soups. The crushed leaves can

be placed over cuts and abrasions and used to soothe the skin after insect bites and stings. The leaves may also be made into a compress and applied to painful areas in cases of gout, rheumatism, inflamed skin and varicose veins.

The fruits have diuretic properties and are taken internally, as decoctions and extracts, for kidney and bladder complaints and intestinal diseases. Decoctions of the fruits taken internally may be combined with external treatment of painful areas with fresh leaves. For improving the digestion, finely chopped fresh young leaves with minced beef or porridge are recommended.

> **Extract used as a rectal wash for haemorrhoids:** 20 g ($\frac{3}{4}$ oz) dried leaves scalded in 500 ml (18 fl oz) boiling water. Allow to cool before use.

Aesculus hippocastanum L.
Horse Chestnut

Hippocastanaceae

● This tree grows to a height of up to 30 m (98 ft). It has a broad, richly branched crown. The greyish-brown outer bark of the trunk peels off in flat small plates. The bark on young branches is brown and felty, turning grey later. The stout, spindle-shaped, large pointed buds are covered with sticky brown scales. The opposite leaves are palmate with five to seven leaflets, that are oval and long, rounded off at the tip and narrowed into a wedge shape at the base. They are 20 cm (8 in) long or even longer and irregularly toothed at the edges. They grow on a stout petiole up to 20 cm (8 in) long. The leaf blade is covered with reddish-brown hairs on the underside. These cover the whole surface in young leaves but later run only along the veins. The lateral veins are parallel. The flowers form rich erect panicles. They are symmetrical, white with red or yellow spots with four to five petals and seven stamens. The superior, felty and glandular ovary matures into a large, rounded, prickly capsule (1), containing one to three reddish-brown, glossy seeds (2).

● The Horse Chestnut was introduced from the Balkans and Asia Minor into central and western Europe in the 16th century. It is frequently cultivated as an ornamental tree.

The medicinal constituents are in the young bark, the flowers, the young leaves and the seeds. In March peel the bark from the trimmed branches and dry it as quickly as possible in the sun or by artificial heat. During drying it gives off an ammonia-like smell. Dry the flowers naturally in the shade or in artificial heat at temperatures up to 35 °C (95 °F). Store in well-sealed containers. The young, soft leaves can be dried in the same way as the flowers. Turn small leaves (rusty on the underside) downwards. Dry mature seeds in two stages. Initially, dry them in the air, spread out in a thin layer. Then dry them out fully in artificial heat at a temperature of 60 °C (140 °F). The active constituent of the seeds is ecsin and of the bark is aesculin. These are used to treat poor activity of the veins.

In popular healing the bark is used for treating biliousness. Extracts or decoctions made from the flowers have astringent properties. The fresh leaves, scalded with hot water, are placed externally on contusions. Decoctions or extracts made from the seeds are also used, externally only, as compresses for rheumatic pain, as cosmetic astringents and as bath additives.

Alcoholic extract for rubbing on in cases of rheumatism and gout: add 30 g (1 oz) chopped seeds to 250 ml (9 fl oz) alcohol and leave to stand in the sun for a week.

Decoction for biliousness: add 40 g (1 $\frac{2}{3}$ oz) crushed, dried bark to 400 ml (14 fl oz) water and boil until half the water has evaporated.
Alternatively: take 5 g ($\frac{1}{5}$ oz) crushed and powdered dried bark five times a day.

Agrimonia eupatoria L.
Agrimony

Rosaceae

● Agrimony is a perennial herb 50−80 cm (20−31 in) tall, with a slanting simple or branched rhizome. In its first year the plant produces only a basal rosette of leaves. An erect, branched, densely hairy stem grows from this the following year. The alternate, odd-pinnate leaves grow only on the lower part of the stem. The leaflets are oval and roughly toothed at the margin. The blade is green and slightly hairy above, with a dense, grey, hairy cover on the underside. The flowers grow on short stalks in long, slender terminal spikes. They have a pronounced green, conical calyx, covered with slender, hooked bristles, five yellow petals, ten stamens and a pistil with two styles (1). The fruits are small achenes enclosed in a hardened calyx. The plants flower from June to September and are quite variable according to habitat. The cultivated plants are stouter and less hairy. Scented Agrimony (*Agrimonia procera*) is a similar species.

● Agrimony grows on fairly dry meadows and pastures, along roadsides, in thickets and in open places in dry deciduous woods. It flourishes best in light loamy soils. It is cultivated for pharmaceutical purposes. The seeds are sown in a fine tilth 2−3 cm ($\frac{3}{4}$−1 in) deep in rows 30 cm (1 ft) apart. They must freeze prior to germination. The young plants are thinned to a distance of 30 cm (1 ft) apart. Weed, hoe and water in dry weather.

The entire haulm of the flowering plant is collected. It is cut off, leaving the lower part of the stem with the lower leaves undisturbed, otherwise the plants weaken or die. Dry haulms by hanging them in small bundles or spread them out in thin layers in the shade at a temperature of up to 35 °C (95 °F). There should be no parts of stem thicker than 3 mm ($\frac{1}{10}$ in).

The plant has astringent and anti-inflammatory properties. It stimulates digestion, gall bladder activity and the autonomic nerves. It is used as medicinal teas, macerations or extracts, as a gargle for sore throats and tonsillitis and for rinsing or bathing inflammatory skin conditions.

Maceration for loss of appetite: macerate 3 g ($\frac{1}{10}$ oz) dried haulm in 500 ml (18 fl oz) water.

Decoction for lung infections: boil 15 g ($\frac{1}{2}$ oz) dried haulm in 250 ml (9 fl oz) water for a short while. Take 2−3 cups daily.

Gargle: scald 20 g ($\frac{3}{4}$ oz) dried haulm with 250 ml (9 fl oz) boiling water. Allow to cool before use.

Agropyron repens (L.) P. Beauv.
Couch Grass, Common Couch

 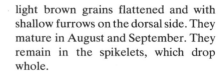

Gramineae

● This is a perennial grass growing up to 150 cm (59 in) tall. It has a jointed, long, creeping and richly branched rhizome. Long, straw- to ochre-coloured lateral shoots grow from the rhizome and penetrate deep into the soil to depths of up to 18 m (59 ft). Erect, glabrous culms grow from nodes on the rhizomes. These are terminated by a sparse narrow spike, up to 10 cm (4 in) long and formed of spikelets (1). The spikelets each contain three to five flowers with two glumes (chafflike bracts). The spikelets are arranged in two rows, so that the spike is flat. Under the glumes are pointed lemmas with either a short spicule at the tip or pointed without a spicule (2). The leaves are alternate, dark green, flat and rough on the upper side. The fruits are light brown grains flattened and with shallow furrows on the dorsal side. They mature in August and September. They remain in the spikelets, which drop whole.

● Couch Grass is a widespread troublesome weed, found in lowland and hilly regions. It flowers in June and July.

Dig up the rhizomes in early spring before the culms sprout, or in the autumn. Remove the soil and rinse thoroughly in running water. Using a stiff brush, remove the small roots, remnants of the culm and any other plants and dead leaves. Dry quickly, either in the sun or in artificial heat at temperatures up to 40 °C (104 °F). Spread the rhizomes out in thin layers and turn frequently. The dry rhizome is straw-coloured, odourless and sweet to the taste. Store the dried rhizomes in bags inside dry, well-sealed containers. Do not allow the rhizomes to become damp as they may be attacked by poisonous moulds. These can be detected as a fine, white to pink coating. They produce toxins that cannot be destroyed by boiling and that interfere with the formation of white blood cells. Anyone taking medicines prepared with mouldy rhizomes is likely to lose his resistance to infections and is particularly prone to purulent forms of tonsillitis.

Couch Grass tea has mild diuretic properties and acts as an expectorant. It is often combined with Chamomile, particularly in children's teas used to treat infections of the urinary tract.

1   2

Diuretic tea: pour 250 ml (9 fl oz) boiling water over 5 ml (1 teaspoon) chopped rhizome and leave to stand for 15 minutes. Drink several times daily.

Alcea rosea L.
Hollyhock

Malvaceae

● This is a biennial (occasionally perennial) ornamental plant up to 3 m (10 ft) tall. In the first year it produces a rich rosette of basal leaves, then in the second year an erect, sparsely branched, hairy stem. The leaves are opposite, rounded in outline, 13–15 cm (5–6 in) long and wide with pronounced veins. They are toothed at the edges. The lower ones have long petioles and are palmately lobed (up to five lobes), the upper leaves have only short petioles and three lobes. The flowers form spike-like clusters at the tip of the stem. They have a green epicalyx divided into six to nine sepals; the calyx has five sepals which are longer than those of the epicalyx. Both the epicalyx and calyx are covered with fine grey-green hairs. There are five petals which may be white, pink, red, yellow or dark reddish-purple. The reddish-violet variety, with a metallic sheen on the petals, is cultivated as a medicinal plant. The numerous stamens are fused into a tube with filaments and attached to the corolla. The anthers are yellow. The pistil has a number of styles. The fruit (1) is round, flattened in the middle, and composed of several flat, round mericarps (2), each containing one seed.

● The Hollyhock originated in southeastern Europe. It flourishes in deep, light, sandy soils with sufficient humus. It grows best in a sheltered position in the sun. The drug is obtained from cultivated plants. Sow the seeds in well-fertilized soil in the autumn, from October to November, or in March. It can either be sown in frames or in beds, 1–2 cm ($\frac{1}{4}$–$\frac{3}{4}$ in) deep. When the seedlings are 10–15 cm (4–6 in) tall, in August or September, plant them out 50 cm (20 in) apart in rows 50 cm (20 in) apart. Seedlings may also be planted out as late as April in the following year.

> **Extract made from the flowers for a disturbed menstrual cycle or as a gargle for sore throats:** infuse 5–10 g ($\frac{1}{5}$–$\frac{2}{5}$ oz) dried petals in 330 ml (12 fl oz) boiling water. Drink in two doses, morning and evening.

For medicinal use, collect either the flower together with calyx and a short flowerstalk, or only the petals. Cut away the flowers before they reach full bloom at the end of June until mid-July. Collect them in dry weather and in sequence up the stem as they open. They are best collected twice daily, in the morning when the dew has dried and in the afternoon. Collecting individual petals, which should be pulled off the flowers by hand, is more time-consuming. Dry them, spread out in thin layers in the shade at temperatures up to 50 °C (122 °F). Store in well-sealed containers.

Hollyhock has anti-inflammatory and mildly curative effects. An extract made with boiling water can be taken for coughs, as the mucilaginous substances it contains protect swollen mucous membranes. The extract can also be used for bathing inflamed skin and for softening the skin. It is also recommended as a gargle to relieve tonsillitis and sore gums.

25

Alchemilla monticola Opiz in Bercht. et Opiz
Lady's Mantle

V–IX

VI–IX

Rosaceae

● This perennial plant has a short rhizome, densely covered with the dry remnants of dead leaf petioles and with brown scales. The rhizome is woody and grows horizontally or at an angle. It dies off progressively at the end and grows again each year at the tip. It produces an abundance of thin roots and a rosette of basal leaves and flowering stems at the tip. The basal leaves have long petioles. They are heart-shaped, dark green, densely covered on both sides with hairs, and divided up to about a quarter into seven to nine broad, oval to round lobes with toothed edges. In the autumn they change colour to reddish-brown.

The stems are curved or erect and covered with spreading hairs. The alternate, short-stalked stem leaves grow out of the axils of cleft stipules. The flowers (1) form dense contracted clusters on short stalks. The fruits are brown, oval achenes.

● Lady's Mantle grows abundantly on lowland and upland meadows and pastures and on the edges of woodland and along streams. There are many similar species and they do not differ from one another from the point of view of curative purposes. It has had a good reputation in popular healing from time immemorial.

Collect the basal leaf rosettes, the whole haulm or the apexes of the flowering stems. It may be used both dried and fresh, internally and externally. It is dried in the shade. It is odourless and has a bitter, astringent taste.

The active constituents relax cramp-like spasm in some muscles, have astringent properties and a beneficial effect on digestion. Compresses made from the scalded fresh leaves help to heal wounds. In Romania, an extract made from the leaves is used as an irrigation to treat persistent diarrhoea and a decoction is taken for the same purpose. In Poland, a decoction made from the flowering tips is used to bathe carbuncles and minor inflammatory skin conditions, and is taken internally for digestive problems, to improve the appetite and as a tranquillizer.

1

> **Extract for diarrhoea:** Boil 10 ml (2 teaspoons) dried, chopped haulm with 200 ml (7 fl oz) boiling water. Take 2 cups during the day.

26

IV–VI

VII–VIII

Alliaria petiolata (M.B.) Cavara et Grande
Garlic Mustard

Cruciferae

● This biennial (sometimes perennial) plant grows to a height of 30–100 cm (1–3 ft). In the first year it produces clusters of heart-shaped leaves with long petioles. They are irregularly toothed at the edges. In the second year, early in spring, an erect, simple or sparsely branched stem grows; it has a glabrous upper part, the lower part often being covered with scant spreading hair, or having a white, powdery appearance. The stem leaves are narrow and glabrous with short petioles. They are triangular to oval, with a heart-shaped indentation at the petiole. The edges are irregularly toothed. The whole plant has a pronounced smell of garlic, particularly when rubbed. The calyx is longer than the flower stalks and the white petals are 5–7 mm ($\frac{1}{5}$–$\frac{3}{5}$ in) long (1). The flowers are crowded at the top of the stalk or on the lateral branches in spikes which lengthen markedly during growth. The stamens bear yellow anthers. The fruit is a pod which grows on a stalk at an angle from the stem (2). It opens into two parts and contains long, oval to almost cylindrical brown seeds.

● Garlic Mustard grows in shaded deciduous and mixed woodland, in hedgerows, neglected gardens and parks, along roadsides and even on rubbish heaps, on lowlands and uplands. It flowers from the end of April to the beginning of June.

The fresh leaves or the whole haulm have medicinal properties. Collect them from April to June; collect the ripe seeds from July to August. The leaves, which have a bitter, burning taste, can be used in salads and meat dishes. They contain vitamins and constituents with an anti-inflammatory effect.

This plant was put to substantial medicinal use in the past. An extract was made from the leaves scalded with hot water; if cold water was used, the leaves were first soaked in edible oil. This extract used to be given for asthma. Decoctions and extracts were taken for diarrhoea and biliousness and to prevent intestinal parasites. Garlic Mustard was also a popular cure for intestinal and vaginal infections. When fresh leaves were not available, a powder made from the crushed seeds was used as a substitute. When this powder was inhaled it made people sneeze, so it was also used in cases of fainting, epilepsy and cramps, rather like smelling salts.

Positive effects are attributed to the sap from the fresh leaves or to compresses made with the powdered fresh seeds in cases of inflammatory skin complaints, particularly slow-healing ulcers.

Allium sativum L.
Garlic

 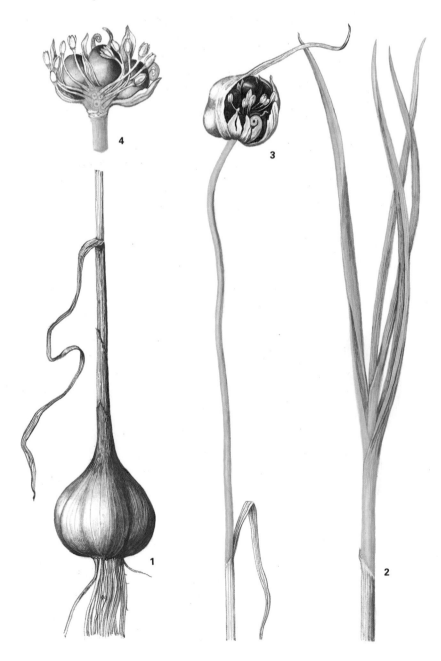

Liliaceae

● The bulb (1) of this perennial plant is composed of large oval cloves which are pointed at the top, wrapped in a hard skin and fixed to a common corky part out of which the little roots grow. The cloves are wrapped in a common, membranous covering consisting of several layers. The stem is unbranched, round and glabrous. The leaves have no stalks and are furrowed and flat, greyish green, pointed at the tip and up to 12 mm ($\frac{1}{2}$ in) wide (2). The young flowers are enveloped in a membranous spathe (3) with a greatly elongated tip; later they form a sparse umbel. They are dirty white, light pink or greenish in colour. Each flower has six free, tapering sepals and six stamens attached by their widened filaments to the perianth. The superior ovary is formed by three capsules. The seeds are glossy and black. Small globular offset-bulbs (4) grow on the umbel and may also grow at the base of the stem.

● Garlic originates from Asia and is widely cultivated as a flavouring. It occasionally grows wild on rubbish dumps etc. from cloves discarded with the dry haulms. It flourishes in heavy, deep soil in a warm, sunny position. It is propagated by planting the individual cloves directly in beds, 15 cm (6 in) apart in rows 20 cm (8 in) apart. Very many varieties of Garlic have been cultivated and these are classified into two categories. The winter varieties yield the larger crop and are planted, 6−8 cm (2−3 in) deep, at the end of September and in the first half of October. The spring varieties are planted, 5−6 cm (2−2 $\frac{1}{2}$ in) deep, in early spring, ideally in March. The beds need to be weeded and hoed. Watering is only necessary in particularly dry weather.

Garlic is harvested in July when the haulm is turning yellow and beginning to dry. Shorten the roots; the haulms may also be removed. Dry the bulbs by hanging them in the shade in bundles of 15−20 plants. Complete the drying process by spreading out the Garlic in thin layers in a cool place.

The fleshy part of the cloves contains anti-bacterial substances which may also be effective against some viral diseases. The cloves may simply be eaten as a vegetable or used to make extracts for special preparations. The fresh juice is effective against parasitic worms and disinfects the intestines in general. It may also be taken to prevent arteriosclerosis. Garlic essence is produced commercially by steam distillation. This thick yellow to yellowish-green liquid smells strongly.

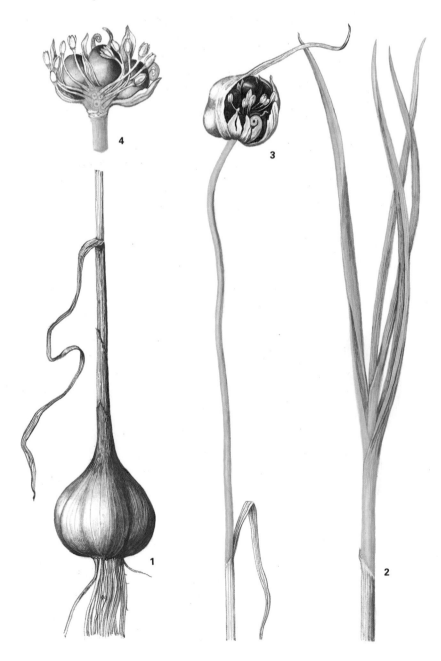

Allium ursinum L.
Wild Garlic

Liliaceae

● This perennial plant grows to a height of 20–50 cm (8–10 in). The elongated white or yellowish bulb is about 2–3 cm ($\frac{3}{4}$–1 in) long (1). The stem is leafless, triangular, slender, soft and green. Usually only two leaves grow directly from the bulb. These are tapering and about 20 cm (8 in) long and 2–5 cm ($\frac{3}{4}$–2 in) wide, narrowing towards the base into a fragile petiole. They are pointed at the tip. The blade is entire and sometimes slightly wavy at the edges. The flowers are arranged in a globose umbel, which, when young, is enclosed in a spathe composed of two to three membranous white inward-curving bracts that drop after flowering. The umbel does not contain offshoot-bulbs, only flowers, which are snow-white and grow on green stalks. The perianth consists of six tapering, pointed, broadly open petals. The stamens have anthers on tapering filaments. A capsule, divided into three receptacles containing black, shiny seeds, develops from the globose ovary.

● Wild Garlic usually grows abundantly in damp, shaded, deciduous woods, mainly in upland beechwoods, but also in meadow woodland or along woodland streams. It is very easy to cultivate in a shady location in the garden and flourishes under hazel trees. It can be grown from seed sown directly in position or from cloves.

Its healing properties are identical with those of Garlic and it is highly valued in popular healing. The fresh green leaves and cloves have anti-bacterial and disinfectant properties and can be used both internally and externally. They are used preventively against infectious diseases. The fresh, chopped leaves can be added to soups or eaten mixed with cottage cheese. Crushed cloves can be added to milk — 1 clove to 100 ml (3 $\frac{1}{2}$ fl oz) milk, taken 1–3 times daily. Water or alcohol extracts are produced from the cloves for infectious, feverish diseases. Compresses from the crushed fresh leaves or cloves may be placed on inflamed skin.

Alnus glutinosa (L.) GAERTN.
Alder

Betulaceae

● This tree grows to heights of 25–30 m (80–90 ft) and has a slender trunk. The branches are erect when young and later become horizontal or drooping. The blackish-green young bark later cracks into small plates to become a greyish-brown to almost black outer bark. The shoots are triangular to round in shape, glabrous, red to olive brown, with a whitish powder at the tips. The buds are alternate, club-shaped and brownish-violet to reddish. They grow on small stalks. The leaves are alternate, oval or round and bluntly notched to indented at the tip, narrowing to a wedge-shape towards the petiole. They are coarsely toothed, rich green and glabrous on the upper side (sticky when young), lighter on the underside and hairy along the veins. The catkins appear from February to April before leaves. The catkin anthers are long and pendent (1), the pistils erect and cone-like (2). The winged fruits are situated in pairs under the scales of the cones when the latter become woody (3). The oval cones are green when young, later dark brown and, after reaching maturity in October, almost black.

● The Alder grows throughout Europe, from the Mediterranean to Scandinavia, and in North Asia, as far as east of Siberia. It grows in damp to marshy places, in lowlands and uplands, along streams and rivers, at springs, in marshes and beside ponds and lakes. It will grow at heights of up to 700 m (2,200 ft) above sea level.

Peel the smooth bark from branches in early spring, when it is easily detached. Dry it in the sun or in drying sheds. The leaves can be collected throughout the growing period and the mature cones from October to February. Cut off the entire slender ends of small branches, together with the cones, and begin drying naturally. Complete the drying process with artificial heat after detaching the cones from the branches.

An extract is prepared from the cones and a decoction from the bark. These are taken for both acute and chronic intestinal inflammation, persistent diarrhoea and dysentery and as a supplement to antibiotics. They can be used as a substitute for oak bark (see page 142).

Extract from alder cones: macerate 10 g ($\frac{2}{5}$ oz) dried cones in 200 ml (7 fl oz) hot water. Take one spoonful three or four times daily.

Decoction from the bark: boil 10 g ($\frac{2}{5}$ oz) crushed bark in 200 ml (7 fl oz) water for a short time. Take three or four times daily.

Althaea officinalis L.
Marsh Mallow

Malvaceae

● Marsh Mallow is a robust, perennial plant 60–150 cm (2–5 ft) tall. It has a fleshy, simple or branched, dirty yellow to brown root (1). In the first year it grows a non-flowering stem with leaves, and from the second year an erect, simple or sparsely branched flowering stem, which is angular at the top and densely covered with hairs. The stem terminates in a sparse raceme of flowers. The leaves grow on short petioles, the lower ones being three- or five-lobed, the upper ones pointed and oval, with heart-shaped indentations. They are irregularly toothed at the edges. The blade is covered with velvety hair on both sides. The flowers grow on short stalks. The green epicalyx consists of six to nine inward-turned bracts which are joined up to half their length Inside this is the calyx consisting of sepals about twice the length of the epicalyx. The corolla is formed by five white to light pink, silky, shiny petals with a shallow indentation at the top. The stamens are numerous, fused, and bear violet anthers. The disc-shaped fruit (2) disintegrates into 10–18 grey, single-seeded kidney-shaped nutlets.

● The Marsh Mallow originates from the eastern Mediterranean and grows wild in warm positions, most frequently in coastal hedgerows or on damp meadows and pastures. It flowers from July to September. It is cultivated for medicinal purposes from seeds and root cuttings in light humus-rich soil. It requires calcium and ground humidity and a sunny position.

Collect the leaves in June and July before the plant starts flowering. Pull them off from the base of the stem in sequence. Collect the flowers in dry weather in July and August. Before harvesting the roots, strengthen them by cutting off the haulm. Dig them up from October to November or in spring from March to April. Dry the leaves and flowers, immediately after harvesting,

in the shade at a temperature of up to 50 °C (122 °F). Turn the leaves, but not the flowers, during drying. Clean the roots of two- to three-year-old plants; peel the tougher ones and slice lengthwise. Dry them in the shade at a temperature of up to 40 °C (104 °F).

The mucilage in the plant relieves coughing and soothes sore throats. An extract made from the root, leaves or flowers can be drunk as an auxiliary preparation for relief from the symptoms of whooping cough, catarrh and sore throats. It is also recommended for intestinal complaints and for diarrhoea, especially in children. It may be used as a gargle for tonsillitis and inflamed gums.

Cough mixture: macerate 20 ml (4 teaspoons) coarsely crushed dry root, or 10 ml (2 teaspoons) flowers and leaves in 500 ml (18 fl oz) water.

31

Anethum graveolens L.
Dill

Umbelliferae

● Dill is an annual herb, 50–120 cm (20–47 in) tall. The root (3) is slender, spindle-shaped, whitish and slightly branched. The stem is erect, cylindrical, hollow, finely furrowed, with small white bands and branched in the upper part. The leaves are alternate and divided three to four times into thin, pinnate sections. They are petiolate in the lower part of the stem. On the upper part they do not have petioles, but a broad sheath envelops the stem. The stem and branches terminate in compound umbels up to 15 cm (6 in) wide with 30–50 rays which have neither covering nor capsules. They contain small, bisexual flowers with an inconspicuous calyx (1). The petals are a rich egg-yellow, narrowing towards the top and shallowly indented. Their ends tend to turn towards the inside of the flower. The pistil has a short style terminating in a slightly globose, widened stigma. The fruits develop into oval to round, flattened achenes (2). They are compressed together in pairs, yellowish brown to reddish brown, and have a thin, yellowish seam at the edge. The whole plant has a distinctive smell.

● Dill probably originates from the Near East, but was already cultivated by the Ancient Egyptians. In Europe it is used as a flavouring. It grows wild on rubbish heaps and in coastal hedgerows. The leaves can be eaten fresh as a vegetable, or preserved in vinegar or salt. Both the stems and the flowers can be used as a flavouring, as well as the seeds.

The seeds germinate early and Dill grows very quickly, so it is possible to obtain several crops in one year. Therefore, it is sown from April until the end of August.

It has diuretic properties, stimulates the appetite and is said to help stomach complaints and flatulence. An extract made from the fruits is helpful in the treatment of stomach ulcers. Tea made from the flowering plant is recommended for urinary complaints and for coughs, particularly when taken in combination with other plants, such as Melilot. It is said to stimulate the production of milk in both humans and cattle. An extract may be taken for headaches, earache and insomnia; a decoction may be helpful in some types of asthma and a decoction made from the fruits and the whole haulm can be taken to prevent arteriosclerosis.

Extract for insomnia: infuse 10 ml (2 teaspoons) fruits in 200 ml (7 fl oz) hot water. Drink in the evening.

Diuretic extract: infuse 5 ml (1 teaspoon) in 200 ml (7 fl oz) hot water. Take 100 ml (3½ fl oz) two to three times a day in gulps.

Angelica archangelica L.
Garden Angelica

Umbelliferae

● Angelica is a biennial plant 100–200 cm (40–80 in) tall. Basal leaves, reaching a length of up to 90 cm (36 in), grow from the stout, branched roots (3) in the first year. They are triangular in shape, pinnately divided two to three times and composed of oval, tapering leaflets. These are pointed or asymmetrically divided into two or three lobes at the top. At the base, the petiole widens into a broad sheath. In the second year a thick, beet-like root forms. It is richly branched at the bottom and coloured dark brown to greyish-brown. The root produces a leafy, thick, hollow, furrowed, glabrous, richly branched stem. The leaves are alternate, glabrous and bluish-green underneath. The lower ones are two to three times pinnate, the upper ones simply odd-pinnate, without a petiole and with a large swollen sheath. The stem and branches terminate in large umbels (4). Each of these consists of 20–40 dense umbels, semi-globose in shape. The flowers have an inconspicuous calyx and a yellowish to greenish corolla (1). The double fruits are broadly oval with three prominent ribs and wings at the edges (2).

● The plant grows wild on mountains near springs above the upper tree line and along mountain streams. It is perennial and frequently flowers only in the third or fourth year. It has been almost destroyed by over-collection and now, therefore, deserves our protection.

The drug is obtained mainly from cultivated plants. Sow the seeds in a cold frame and prick out into deep, damp, loamy soil. Cut back the flower heads to strengthen the roots – the part usually used for home medicines. The fruits may also be used, in which case do not cut back.

The roots are harvested in the autumn of the second year. Wash them and dry them whole at a temperature of up to 40 °C (104 °F). Collect the fruits by

cutting off the umbels before maturity, rubbing off the winged seed cases and then drying them out. The fresh haulm, fruits and roots contain chemicals which destroy the skin's natural protection from sunlight, so always wear gloves when handling the plant and wash your hands thoroughly immediately afterwards.

Garden Angelica has a marked diuretic effect and stimulates sweating, digestion and the appetite. It also acts as a tranquillizer and has proved its worth in cases of insomnia. Bathing with the extract can help ease muscular pains and a vinegar extract can be applied to swellings and contusions. Angelica is also used in the manufacture of liqueurs and confectionery.

> **Vinegar extract for swellings and contusions:** macerate 20 g ($\frac{3}{4}$ oz) crushed roots or seed cases in 250 ml (8 fl oz) vinegar for 36 hours. Apply compresses soaked in the extract.

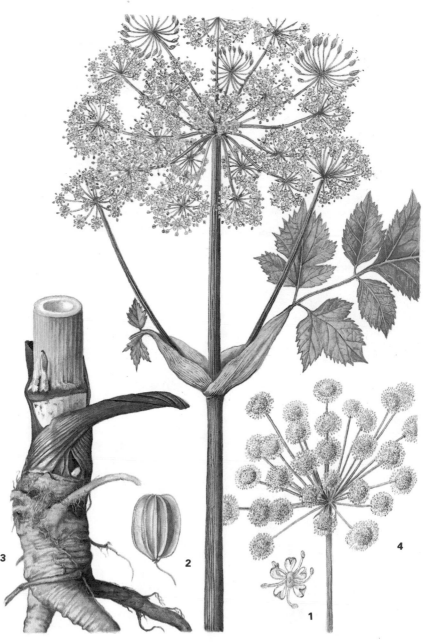

33

Anthyllis vulneraria L.
Kidney Vetch

VI–VII 🌿
V–VIII ✳

Leguminosae

● Kidney Vetch is a perennial plant with stems up to 40 cm (16 in) tall. The slender, branched rhizome bears rosettes of basal leaves at the tips. These are sparsely and asymmetrically odd-pinnate, the leaflet at the tip being oval and much bigger than the lateral leaflets. The stems are erect, scantily branched and hairy. The upper part has an almost white woolly cover. The leaves are alternate, sparse, odd-pinnate and very varied in shape. The small stipules grow together with the petiole. The entire blade is either glabrous or covered with thin hairs; the underside is covered with fine silky hairs. The stem and lateral branches each bear one or two umbel-like inflorescences, concentrated in dense heads. They grow out of bracts divided into three to seven lobes. The flowers (1) have either no flower stalk or only very short stalks. The calyx is velvety to woolly, dingy white or yellow in colour, sometimes reddish at the top, with inconspicuous veins. At the top it is divided into five teeth. The corolla is yellow to red.

● It grows on dry grassland, shrubby slopes and in sparse woodland, sometimes even on rocks. It used to be cultivated for animal fodder and has now spread to grow wild in some places. Upland plants, which deviate in colour, are mostly classified as subspecies. No distinction is made between these different Kidney Vetches from the point of view of medicinal value.

The dried inflorescence or the whole haulm is used. The plant can also be used fresh, the scalded and cooled haulm being placed on wounds or inflamed skin to treat such conditions as abscesses, spots and eczema. It makes a useful home cosmetic for cleansing and softening the skin; a decoction prepared from the fresh or dried plant can be added to the bath. Gargle with a decoction to soothe a sore throat and use as a mouth rinse for inflamed gums. It has somewhat astringent and mildly disinfectant properties. It is said to help renew mucous membrane cells in the throat and mouth. Tea made from the dried flowers can substitute for ordinary tea, but bear in mind that it is mildly laxative.

1

Tea: infuse 15 ml (1 tablespoon) dried flowers in 250 ml (9 fl oz) water for 15 minutes. Drink the tea in several doses during the day.

Arctium tomentosum Mill.
Woolly Burdock

Compositae

● This biennial plant grows to a height of more than 100 cm (39 in). It has a large, cylindrical root (1). A rosette of basal leaves (2) grows in the first year and an erect, richly branched, deeply furrowed, woolly stem grows in the second year. The leaves are alternate, petiolate, heart-shaped, entire or lobed and toothed at the edges. The blade is glabrous or downy on the upper side, but the underside is densely covered with white velvety hair. The globose flower heads have a cobwebbed, white, woolly ring composed of inwardly turned bracts which are shorter than the flowers. The bracts, often tinged violet, are bristly and toothed at the edges. Most terminate in a hook-like spike, the inner ones with only a straight point. The flowers are violet with a corolla divided into five lobes, with a pistil and five stamens. The pistil has a two-lobed stigma with a ring of hairs. The fruits are somewhat flattened, furrowed, and transversely wrinkled achenes.

● Woolly Burdock grows along road-sides, on rubbish dumps, in hedgerows and on waste ground close to human habitation. It flourishes in rich loamy soils with a substantial nitrogen content, particularly on limestone or chalk.

The roots of plants that have not yet come into flower are used in popular medicine. These are collected in the first year in autumn or in the second year in early spring. The roots of flowering plants are useless because they are woody and often decayed and hollow. This makes them susceptible to attack by insects, moulds and bacteria. Wash the roots thoroughly and cut the thicker ones in half lengthwise. Dry at a temperature of up to 40 °C (104 °F). When correctly dried, they are fragile and not blackened. The leaves are also used in popular healing. Sometimes even the fruits are collected for the manufacture of an oil.

An extract or decoction made from the dried root is useful for digestive disorders and as a diuretic preparation for people with kidney stones. It also stimulates sweating. It is effective in preventing spots and may also be used as a mouth rinse or gargle. It encourages hair growth. A decoction made from the leaves may be used to bathe abscesses, as a gargle and mouth rinse, and can be taken internally for digestive disorders.

Decoction for compresses and gargles: add 30 g (1 oz) dried leaves to 500 ml (18 fl oz) water and boil for 5 minutes.

Decoction to be taken for digestive disorders: add 10 g ($\frac{2}{3}$ oz) dried leaves to 500 ml (18 fl oz) water and boil for 2 minutes.

2

1

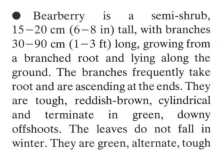

Arctostaphylos uva-ursi (L.) SPRENG.
Bearberry

Ericaceae

● Bearberry is a semi-shrub, 15—20 cm (6—8 in) tall, with branches 30—90 cm (1—3 ft) long, growing from a branched root and lying along the ground. The branches frequently take root and are ascending at the ends. They are tough, reddish-brown, cylindrical and terminate in green, downy offshoots. The leaves do not fall in winter. They are green, alternate, tough and leathery, oval in shape and round at the ends, narrowing towards the short petiole into a wedge shape. They are entire, flat, shiny and dark green on the upper side. The underside is lighter in colour, and has conspicuous net-like veins. The edges and petioles are imperceptibly downy. Flowers, in groups of three to ten in short pendent clusters, grow on short stalks from the axils of two small bracts at the tips of the small branches. The flowers are regular and bisexual. The calyx is deeply divided into five blunt lobes. The oval corolla is bulbous and split into five short, backward-bending lobes at the top. There are five stamens with red anthers. The superior ovary with its long stigma matures into a red drupe.

● Bearberry grows in dry pine forests, on heaths, grassland and on rocky slopes. It flowers from April to June. It is rare, and protected in most European countries.

It is best propagated from cuttings. When they have rooted, they should be separated from the parent plant and, as far as possible, replanted with the soil attached to the roots. Bearberry requires permeable soil. It can also be propagated from cuttings in a frame or a cold glasshouse, where rooting is encouraged by means of hormone rooting powder. When propagating from seeds, it is essential to soak the mature fruits in water for 24 hours. The seeds are then rinsed with water and sown in frames in a light soil mixed with sand and peat. The seeds germinate very irregularly and often only after a long time. Prick out the seedlings to 20 cm (8 in) apart.

For medicinal purposes, collect the leaves by pulling them off the non-flowering small branches or off the lower part of the flowering branches. Dry them as quickly as possible in the shade.

The plant is used to treat inflammation of the urinary tract, which it disinfects, turning the urine green. It stimulates the kidneys to eliminate salt and has astringent properties. In contrast with many other medicinal plants, the active constituents are only released after 15—30 minutes of boiling in water.

Decoction for inflammation of the urinary tract: add 40 g (1 $\frac{2}{5}$ oz) dried leaves to 500 ml (18 fl oz) water and boil for 15—30 minutes.

III–XI

 V–IX

Armoracia rusticana

PH. GAERTN., B. MEY et SCHERB.

Horseradish

Cruciferae

● Horseradish is a perennial plant growing to a height of 150 cm (59 in). It has a long, perpendicular root, 2–3 cm ($\frac{3}{4}$–1 in) thick; it is even thicker in cultivated plants grown under good conditions. In wild plants, the root is often more branched, red-brown on the surface and white inside, with multiple heads above in older plants. The root produces rosettes of basal leaves. The elongated blade is wavy, coarsely toothed at the edge with a heart-shaped indentation at the petiole, and has thick, prominent veins. The leaves, borne on richly branched stems, are alternate and mostly without petioles. Only those on the lower part of the stem have short petioles. They are tapering in outline and often divided into bluntly ended pinnate sections. The flowers are arranged in a raceme. The petals are white and two to three times the length of the green calyx. This consists of four elongated oval, white-edged sepals, which are round at the tip. The fruits are double capsuled, ovate pods, pointed at the tip.

● Horseradish originates from eastern Europe. It has been cultivated for many centuries throughout the whole of Europe and has gone wild in many places, growing not only near fences and in ditches, but along streams and river banks and in damp undergrowth.

It is very widely used in popular medicine. The fresh leaves are used externally only, the fresh root is used both externally and internally. Bruised fresh leaves can be placed on varicose veins, but must not be left for long. After a few minutes the skin reddens and a burning sensation becomes apparent. After prolonged application, blisters may appear. Similar skin damage may be caused by so-called horseradish cakes, which are made from the grated root and flour. Wrapped in linen, they are placed on painful areas, for a maximum of half an hour, to relieve discomfort in cases of rheumatism, pleurisy and other complaints. The juice from the grated and pressed root is very effective in treating coughs and hoarseness. Take 5 ml (1 teaspoon) three times a day with honey, sugar or bread. Horseradish root has diuretic properties and it also contains chemicals that repress the reproduction of numerous species of bacteria, some fungi, protozoa and viruses. Apple and horseradish relish is often served with steak and roast beef.

Apple and horseradish relish: mix together 500 g (1 lb) grated apple, 30 g (1 oz) horseradish, 50 g (1 $\frac{3}{4}$ oz) sugar and 20 ml (4 teaspoons) vinegar.

Horseradish extract for digestive disorders: chop 100 g (3 $\frac{1}{2}$ oz) root into small pieces. Add to 1 litre (1 $\frac{3}{4}$ pints) wine and boil for 2 minutes.

Arnica montana L.
Arnica

 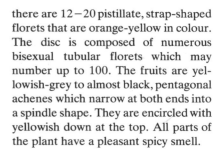
Compositae

Arnica is a protected plant. It is a perennial with a creeping, branched rhizome. A rosette of basal leaves grows in the first year. The leaves are quite tough, oval, entire and covered with short hair. They have five to seven prominent longitudinal veins. In subsequent years, erect simple or slightly branched stems grow from the basal rosette. They may be up to 50 cm (20 in) tall. They are covered with short hairs and bear one to three pairs of opposite leaves. The stem and branches terminate in large flower heads, opening from May to August. Around the periphery there are 12–20 pistillate, strap-shaped florets that are orange-yellow in colour. The disc is composed of numerous bisexual tubular florets which may number up to 100. The fruits are yellowish-grey to almost black, pentagonal achenes which narrow at both ends into a spindle shape. They are encircled with yellowish down at the top. All parts of the plant have a pleasant spicy smell.

Arnica grows on damp upland meadows, near springs, on marshes and on damp, sparse heaths. At lower elevations, it does well on calcium-free soils. It dies out in manured and intensively farmed fields, although it flourishes in meadows grazed by cattle because they avoid it. Arnica is protected in many countries and it is often only permissible to collect the flowers. Home medical treatments are, therefore, prepared from cultivated plants.

It is cultivated from the achenes. Store them in a cool, damp place in winter so that they do not lose their ability to germinate. Sow in the early spring; they will germinate within two to three weeks. The seeds can be sown in a frame in August and the seedlings planted in spring, 25 cm (10 in) apart in rows 30 cm (12 in) apart. The plants flower in the second year and are harvested in the autumn of the third year.

Dry the flower heads or the whole haulm at a temperature of 40 °C (104 °F) to kill off the fly larvae living in the flower heads. Wash the rhizomes thoroughly and dry them in the sun or by artificial heat at a maximum temperature of 70 °C (158 °F). The flowers, without the bracts and receptacles, are the most useful part of the plant.

Commercial medicines are manufactured from the dried flowers. These are used to treat skin inflammations and for healing wounds. Medicines are taken internally for diseases of the respiratory passages and the digestive system and for disturbances in the menstrual cycle. Home-made medicines based on Arnica are not recommended and can be very dangerous. An incorrect dose can cause skin rashes, inflammation of the mucous membranes or severe intestinal inflammation.

Artemisia absinthium L.
Wormwood

Compositae

● Wormwood is a perennial, bitter, aromatic herb growing to a height of 60–100 cm (24–39 in). It has a multi-headed rhizome and the lower part of the stem is woody. A tuft of basal leaves and one to several stalks grow from each head of the rhizome. The basal leaves, which are on long petioles and pinnately three times divided, partly survive the winter. The blades are oval in shape, silvery grey, covered in dense hair and dotted with glands. The stalks are also light grey and felty, richly branched and terminating in panicles of numerous tiny flower heads. They are covered with alternate leaves, the lower ones being stalked and bipinnate, the upper ones without stalks and divided into one pinnate section. These transform into undivided tapering bracts. The almost globose flower heads grow on short stalks, and have grey, felty, inwardly turned, tapering and ovate bracts. The receptacle is covered with rough hair. The peripheral pistillate and the inner bisexual flowers (1) are tubular and yellow in colour. All of these mature into oval, greyish-brown, finely striped achenes.

● Wormwood grows in warmer regions on rocks, screes, dry shrubby slopes and, to a lesser extent, beside roads and railway lines. It also grows on the edges of villages, having escaped from gardens to grow wild. It flourishes on soils which are rich in calcium and nitrogen. In the past it was frequently cultivated in gardens, not only as a medicinal plant, but also as a flavouring for home-made wines and liqueurs. It is now known that the regular consumption of alcoholic drinks containing Wormwood can cause severe health disorders. Commercial drinks, such as absinthe, have therefore been banned in many countries. As a medicinal herb, properly used, it is very valuable.

Extract: infuse 2 g ($\frac{3}{4}$ oz) dried Wormwood in 250 ml (9 fl oz) hot water for several minutes. Drink unsweetened, several times daily. Do not take for prolonged periods nor exceed the dose.

Collect the whole haulm when in flower or shortly before flowering from June to August. Sometimes, the haulm can be collected as many as three times a year, since the cut-back plants produce new shoots which are very rich in active substances. Cut the haulm only during dry, sunny weather. The basal leaves may also be collected. Dry them spread out in thin layers or hung in small bundles in the shade at a temperature of up to 40 °C (104 °F). Store in well-sealed containers.

An extract is used for digestive and intestinal problems and as a gargle. It can be made more palatable with cinnamon. Excessive and permanent use of Wormwood damages the nervous system. Preparations made with Wormwood should never be used by pregnant women.

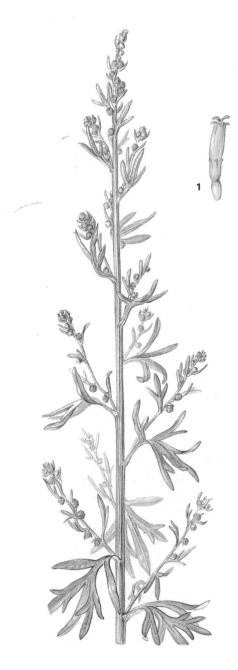

Artemisia vulgaris L.
Mugwort

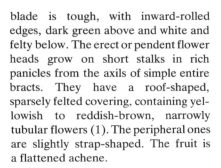
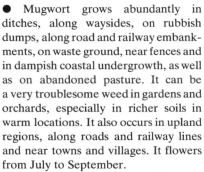

VII–IX

X

Compositae

● This is a robust, aromatic perennial plant. Numerous richly branched roots grow from the short rhizome. It has several erect, thick, hard and prominently furrowed, reddish-brown to purplish stems, up to 150 cm (59 in) tall. These are richly branched and downy on the surface with pulp inside. The leaves are alternate, with a broadly oval blade. The lower ones grow on short petioles, with small ears at the petiole and are bipinnately lobed. The upper leaves are simply pinnate. They are divided into tapering entire or serrate sections, pointed at the ends. The section at the tip is large and has three lobes. The blade is tough, with inward-rolled edges, dark green above and white and felty below. The erect or pendent flower heads grow on short stalks in rich panicles from the axils of simple entire bracts. They have a roof-shaped, sparsely felted covering, containing yellowish to reddish-brown, narrowly tubular flowers (1). The peripheral ones are slightly strap-shaped. The fruit is a flattened achene.

● Mugwort grows abundantly in ditches, along waysides, on rubbish dumps, along road and railway embankments, on waste ground, near fences and in dampish coastal undergrowth, as well as on abandoned pasture. It can be a very troublesome weed in gardens and orchards, especially in richer soils in warm locations. It also occurs in upland regions, along roads and railway lines and near towns and villages. It flowers from July to September.

Collect the haulm when flowering, or the roots (without the rhizome) in October. Cut off the upper parts of the flower heads and those not yet in bloom, at a length of 20–30 cm (8–12 in). Dry them as quickly as possible in the shade, hung in small bundles, at a temperature of up to 40 °C (104 °F). Remove any remnants of the rhizome from the roots and wash them quickly. Dry them in small bundles in a similar way to the haulm. When they are dry, brush them to remove the last remnants of soil or other impurities.

Mugwort is used to treat digestive disorders, loss of appetite, flatulence and menstrual problems. It also acts as a tranquillizer and can help to alleviate insomnia and stomach cramps and to relieve pain. In places where Wormwood does not grow, Mugwort is used as a substitute, both in popular healing and in making liqueurs. Like Wormwood, prolonged use of Mugwort is very dangerous and damages the nervous system.

1

Asarum europaeum L.
Asarabacca

Aristolochiaceae

● This is a perennial plant 5–15 cm (2–6 in) tall, with a creeping, branched, sparsely segmented, almost cylindrical rhizome. Two or three leaves and pendent flowers on short stalks grow each year at the end of the rhizome and its lateral branches. The leaves are entire, heart-shaped, leathery, glabrous and glossy dark green on the upper side, brownish-green on the underside. The flowers have a brownish-green perianth of bulbous shape, composed of three fused petals which are brownish-green on the outer side and a dull purple inside. There are 12 stamens arranged in two circles and an inferior ovary with a thick columnal style and a stigma with six lobes. A six-celled capsule containing three or four seeds in each cell develops from the ovary. The seeds are oval in shape and have a prominent spongy ridge on one side through which the root penetrates when it germinates. The entire plant is characterized by a camphor-like smell.

● Asarabacca grows in shady, humus-rich soil in rather damp deciduous woods, and particularly under hazel trees, and in hedgerows. It also occurs in coniferous forests which have been planted in places where there was formerly deciduous or mixed cover. It flowers from the end of March until May.

Collect the haulm, together with the roots, in May or June, or the root with rhizomes in August. Be careful not to destroy the growing plant. Clean and dry the plants at a temperature of up to 40 °C (104 °F). If you are using the rhizomes only, remove the leaves and capsules before drying.

In the past, this plant was widely used to provoke vomiting and diarrhoea in the case of food poisoning or after eating poisonous fungi, for example. Drops of an essence, known as *Oleum*

asari, were used to treat inflammation of the middle ear. It was also said to have beneficial effects on kidney diseases. Its use was later restricted to veterinary medicine only, but the Polish pharmacopoeia still acknowledges this drug. Azarin tablets and asari tincture, which

are given as expectorants to sufferers from bronchitis, smoker's coughs and silicosis, are produced commercially from Asarabacca. It must not be used to treat emphysema. As the drug is mildly toxic, it should not be used in home medicines.

Atropa belladonna L.
Deadly Nightshade

Solanaceae

● Deadly Nightshade is a robust perennial plant growing to a height of up to 150 cm (59 in). It has a thick, branched rhizome. The erect stems are forked, finely furrowed and covered with soft hair, especially on the upper parts. The almost glabrous leaves are oval, entire, opposite and pointed at the tip, narrowing at the base into a short petiole. The blade has pinnate veins. There are usually two leaves — a larger and a smaller — close to each other. The flowers grow separately on long stalks, or in pairs and threes in a small inflorescence. The five-lobed calyx becomes markedly larger after flowering.

The bell-shaped corolla is brownish-purple or brownish, with a violet tinge outside and greyish-yellow with reddish veins inside. It is divided into five lobes, which are round and bent backwards at the ends. The flower has five stamens with yellow anthers. The filaments are hairy at the base. The pistil has a two-lobed stigma. The fruit is a large, glossy, spherical berry, which is green when young and black after maturing.

● Deadly Nightshade grows in upland deciduous forests, on the edges of woods and in clearings. The alkaline content of the soil is very important. The plant flourishes in black earth and in good humus-rich sandy-loamy soils. It requires water-retentive soil, good fertilization and a supply of calcium. The drug made from plants grown in the shade is less valuable. The flowers open in June and July.

Cultivated plants are used for commercial processing. The seed is obtained by fermenting mature berries for three days, rinsing them with water and then crushing them, or by crushing dried berries. Sow the seeds in autumn after collection or in early spring, in March and April, in rows 60 cm (2 ft) apart. Thin out the seedlings to a distance of 60 cm (2 ft) apart.

Collect the leaves shortly before flowering, during flowering, or even shortly afterwards, that is from June until mid-August. Flowering plants have the best yield. You can dig up the roots of three- or four-year-old plants in September and October. Dry the leaves and roots in thin layers in natural heat in the shade, or by artificial heat up to a temperature of 50 °C (122 °F). All parts of the plant are highly poisonous.

Many medicines are manufactured from Deadly Nightshade. It is used to treat asthma and cramps, and as an antidote to some poisons. Atropine eyedrops used to be used for dilating the pupils during examination of the retina. Deadly Nightshade should never be used in popular healing because it is highly poisonous and can kill.

Bellis perennis L.
Daisy

Compositae

● The Daisy is a low perennial. A rosette of basal leaves grows from the cylindrical rhizome. These are spoon-shaped, rounded at the ends, narrowing downwards into a broad petiole. They are round-toothed and glabrous or with short hairs. The stalks are simple, leafless, erect, finely hairy and up to 15 cm (6 in) tall. Single flower heads grow at the ends of the stems. The flower heads have a conical hollow receptacle with a cup-shaped depression and are without scales. There are two rows of soft green bracts of equal length. They are oval, blunt at the ends and downy. On the periphery are a large number of narrow, strap-shaped, white or pink pistillate ray-florets. The inner disc is formed by bisexual, tubular yellow florets. At night or during rainy weather the ray-florets bend towards the inside and close the flower head. The fruits are smooth achenes without down.

● Daisies grow very abundantly in grass in woods and gardens, on both lowlands and uplands. Large-blossomed varieties, with ray-florets only, are cultivated, but these are not collected for medicinal purposes.

Collect the flower heads before they reach full bloom, so that they do not fall apart while drying. Pick only in dry weather with a maximum 1 cm ($\frac{1}{2}$ in) stalk. Dry, spread out in thin layers in the shade or by artificial heat at a temperature of up to 35 °C (95 °F). The bracts must remain green after drying. Store in well-sealed containers.

Daisy has anti-inflammatory and mildly astringent properties and stimulates digestion. The active constituents have been found in all parts of the plant. It was more widely used in popular healing in the past than it is today, but it is still used for kidney and urinary tract diseases, as a painkiller and to treat rheumatism, gout, liver and gallbladder complaints, dropsy, constipation, digestive disorders and menstrual problems.

The leaves are also sometimes used in popular healing. In Spain, an extract made from the flowers and leaves is taken for bronchial catarrh and used as a gargle to treat sore throats and inflamed gums, whereas in Poland it is used for bathing and to treat skin disorders.

> **Extract for use as a mouth rinse, gargle and for compresses:** infuse 15–25 g ($\frac{1}{2}$ oz) dried flowers in 1 litre (1 $\frac{3}{4}$ pints) cold water for six to eight hours.

Berberis vulgaris L.
Barberry

Berberidaceae

● This thorny shrub is 1–3 m (3–10 ft) tall, with erect branches slightly bent at the ends. The shoots are yellowish-brown and furrowed along their lengths. The older twigs have greyish bark and spines with up to seven points. In the axils, there are often light brown, alternate, ovately edged leaf-buds, often with the remains of old petioles. The leaves are alternate, spoon-shaped and rounded at the ends, narrowing downwards into a wedge shape. They are concentrated in clusters. The blade has spiny teeth, with a prominent nervature on the underside. The yellow, bisexual globular flowers are arranged in pendent racemes. Each has six sepals and six petals. The six stamens bend inwards if touched. The ovary matures into a cylindrical, red berry hanging on a pendent stalk. Each berry contains two to five seeds with a dull, rough, brown skin.

● Barberry grows in central and southern Europe, occurring on rocky slopes and pastures and in more open woodland, chiefly oak-and-hornbeam and oak. It does best on limestone and will grow at elevations of up to 800 m (2,600 ft) above sea level. It flowers after the leaves have sprouted in May.

The roots have medicinal properties. Dig them up in autumn. In thicker roots, only the bark peeled from them is used. Dry the roots and the bark either in the sun or by artificial heat, at a temperature not exceeding 50 °C (122 °F). The bark from the thicker branches also has medicinal properties. Dry it in the same way as the bark from the roots. Collect the fruits before they reach full maturity, in September and October, and dry them naturally in the shade. They contain organic acids and vitamin C. The fresh fruits are processed into syrups, jams, compotes and additives for soft drinks.

Barberry has a mildly laxative and diuretic effect in small doses, increasing the production and excretion of gall and relieving cramplike spasms in some muscles. It is also used to treat diseases of the gallbladder, kidney stones and inflammation of the urinary tract. The bark has a beneficial effect on the circulatory system. All parts of the plant contain toxic alkaloids which, in larger doses, can seriously damage your health. They must not be used without medical supervision.

44

Betonica officinalis L.
Betony

Labiatae

● Betony is a perennial plant with a short branched rhizome. The erect stem is 30—80 cm (12—31 in) tall, usually unbranched, square and coarsely hairy. It has one or two pairs of opposite leaves. The basal leaves are on long petioles and are oblong to oval, round-toothed and rounded at the ends, with a shallow heart-shaped indentation at the petiole. They are glabrous on the upper side and hairy underneath. The lower stem leaves have short petioles, the upper ones none. They are the same shape as the basal leaves but smaller. The stem terminates in a spike-like inflorescence (1) with numerous tapering bracts. The flowers have a bell-shaped five-lobed calyx (2) cleft up to about a third into tapering teeth terminating in a short bristle. The symmetrical, carmine-red corolla has a white, slightly curved tube. The upper lip is erect or bent backwards and is hairy on the outside. The lower lip is divided into three lobes. The central one is large and toothed on the edges and has a shallow heart-shaped indentation, the lateral lobes are rounded. The stamens bear violet-brown anthers. The pistil has a pinkish style and a forked stigma.

● Betony grows in open woodland, on meadows and shrubby slopes on lowlands and uplands. It flowers from May to August.

The flowering haulm with the basal leaves is collected. Harvest in June and July before flowering has finished and dry in natural heat in the shade. Do not turn the plants. Store in a dry place. The dried flower has a distinctive, not particularly pleasant, smell.

Betony is used only in popular healing nowadays, mainly to treat diarrhoea and biliousness. A tea may be drunk to relieve the respiratory disorders, as it facilitates expectoration and loosens mucus. Sweeten the tea with honey or crystallized sugar. Alternatively, take a teaspoonful of herb juice with honey, three times a day. Betony also has a tranquillizing effect on the nervous system and is used to relieve inflammation of the urinary tract. It is most frequently given in the form of an extract made with boiling water or as a powder, and has no negative side-effects. The extract is also used for bathing skin disorders caused by microscopic fungi.

Extract for digestive disorders: infuse 3—5 g ($\frac{1}{10}$—$\frac{1}{5}$ oz) dried flowers in 200 ml (7 fl oz) boiling water for about 15 minutes. To be taken once a day.

45

Betula pendula ROTH
Silver Birch

Betulaceae

● This tree, with an ovate crown and drooping branches, reaches a height of 20—30 m (65—100 ft). It has brown shoots with waxy white pores. The lateral twigs are short, the older ones greyish-brown. The buds are alternate, conical, pointed and greenish-brown to blackish-brown in colour. The white bark of the thicker branches and the trunk peels off in thin, papery strips. On the lower part of the thicker trunk, it changes into a black, fissured outer bark. The leaves are alternate and on long petioles, with kite-shaped blades, lobed at the edges and with long and short teeth. The young leaves are downy and sticky, later they are glabrous with a greyish-green tinge on the underside. The male catkins are drooping and up to 8 cm (3 in) long, with brown bracts and yellow anthers (1). The female catkins are erect or slanting, up to 2 cm ($\frac{3}{4}$ in) long, and light green with purple stigmas (2). They appear at the same time as the leaves, in March and April. The winged fruits are crowded in small disintegrating cones which droop when maturing.

● Silver Birch grows throughout almost the whole of Europe and northern Asia on lowlands and highlands.

The active constituents are found mainly in the leaves. Collect them from May to June and dry them slowly, spread out in thin layers, in the shade. Similar active constituents are also found in the green bark. This can be obtained from the branches, thinner trunks or from the tops of felled trees by peeling off the outer papery bark and separating the green bark from the wood. The dried bark is crushed or ground into a powder. The buds may also be collected before sprouting, and can be substituted for the leaves in home medicines. Dry them in an airy place in the shade or in mild sunlight. An essence obtained from the fresh buds is used in the manufacture of hair lotions. In spring, sap is obtained by drilling the trunks and this is recommended for kidney and bladder ailments and for use as a refreshing drink with a restorative effect. It is also used in cosmetics.

The dried leaves and bark have pronounced diuretic properties, and long-term use of Silver Birch tea can help to dissolve and release kidney stones and to cure gout. It induces mild perspiration and reduces fever. It is recommended in cases of rheumatism and forms part of a mixture used to prevent arteriosclerosis.

Diuretic tea: add some 10—20 g ($\frac{3}{10}$—$\frac{7}{10}$ oz) dried leaves to 500 ml (18 fl oz) water and boil for five minutes. Take in three to four doses during the day.

Extract for gout: macerate 15 leaves in 200 ml (7 fl oz) hot water.

Borago officinalis L.
Borage

Boraginaceae

● This robust annual herb is approximately 60 cm (2 ft) tall. It has an erect, simple or sparsely branched, often reddish stem covered with sparse, spreading, bristly hairs. The basal leaves on long petioles form a rosette. The stem leaves have no petioles and are alternate, tapering ovals, entire or slightly indented and corrugated with prominent veins. The stalked flowers, which hang down in a curve, grow in sparse monochasial cymes from the axils of bracts. They have a five-lobed calyx formed of narrowly tapering sepals which open broadly during the period of flowering and close around the fruit later on. The corolla is wheel-shaped, deeply divided into five oval petals. It is usually blue or, rarely, white in colour. At the mouth of the very short tube it has small white scales. There are five stamens. The violet anthers grow on the inner arm of the short, broad and bifurcated filament. The outer arm is without anthers. The fruits are four light brown, elongatedly ovate, rough mericarps.

● Borage originates from southern Europe. It is cultivated as a culinary herb or a melliferous plant. Sometimes, usually only temporarily, it turns wild in warm regions. It flowers from June to September.

The flowers are obtained from cultivated plants. Borage requires damp, sandy to loamy soil, sufficiently fertile and rich in calcium. It does well in a sunny or semi-shaded position. Sow the seeds in March in rows 25 cm (10 in) apart. They germinate within one to three weeks in the shade, so it is necessary to cover them well with soil. Weed the beds around the seedlings at least twice and aerate the soil several times.

Harvest the whole haulm when the plants are in flower, from June to September. Cut it off above the ground, and remove the dry, brown leaves. Dry it, spread out in thin layers in the shade or by artificial heat up to a temperature of 35 °C (95 °F). Borage has a cucumber-like smell and taste. The dried flowers readily absorb moisture from the air, so they must be kept in well-sealed containers.

It is used to treat sore throats and gums, influenza, coughs and stomach and intestinal disorders. Borage compresses can be applied to inflamed skin. It also softens the skin. Young leaves are added to salads and soups and as a flavouring to sauces.

> **Fever-reducing and diuretic tea:** infuse 20 g (¾ oz) dried flowers pulled off the haulm (possibly with lime flowers and cabbage rose petals) in 300 ml (10 fl oz) hot water for 15 minutes. Drink the warm tea several times a day.

47

Bryonia alba L.
Blackberried Bryony

Cucurbitaceae

● This is a perennial, climbing plant with a 200–400 cm (6 ½ – 13 ft) long stem. The large, often branched beet-like root (1) is a light ochre on the surface, transversely furrowed with irregular spore-like tubercles, and white and fleshy inside. Several angular stems grow from the root. They are glabrous at the bottom and bear sparse, spreading, colourless hairs and are branched at the top. The leaves are alternate and on short petioles. They are palmately five-lobed with triangular tips, with widely spaced teeth on the edges and pointed teeth at the apex. The blade is covered with tough hair. Simple tendrils grow from the leaf axils, by means of which the plant climbs shrubs and trees. The male flowers grow in long-stalked pseudo-racemes, the female ones in short-stalked, concentrated cymes. The calyx is green and five-lobed. The light yellowish-green corolla with a pronounced green nervature is formed of five ovate petals. The fruits are bluish-black berries (2). The whole plant has a nasty smell.

● Bryony is native to southern Europe. Large quantities used to be cultivated in central Europe and it has gone wild or even acclimatized in many places. It grows near fences, in gardens and hedgerows and along streams and rivers. In some places it even grows in permanently inundated woodland. It does particularly well in rich, damper soils, although it can tolerate considerable drought. It flowers in June and July.

The root contains the active constituents. It is a strong laxative, stimulates urination and causes vomiting. As it is a highly poisonous plant, it must never be used for home medicines. The symptoms of Bryony poisoning are stomach irritation, severe colic pain, high fever, rapid superficial breathing and blood in the urine. A powder made of the dried root is used to manufacture diuretic medicines, to eliminate intestinal parasites and to induce vomiting and diarrhoea in some cases of poisoning. It is also used in preparations for treating constipation, flatulence, dropsy, rheumatism and bronchitis.

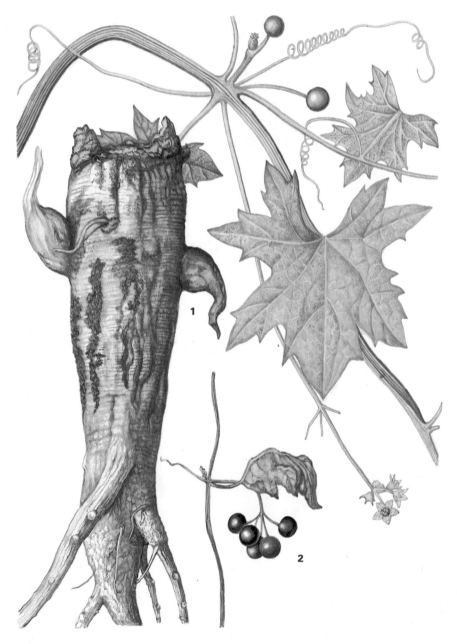

Buxus sempervirens L.
Box

● This evergreen shrub or small tree reaches a height of approximately 1 m (3 ft); old trees may even grow to more than 8 m (26 ft). It has a very dense root system forming a network of thin yellow roots. The bark is yellowish-brown and wrinkled. The outer bark cracks into small flat plates. The branches are hairy when young, and glabrous later. They are angular, olive green and densely covered with opposite leaves growing on short petioles. The leaves are leathery, oval, have a shallow indentation at the tip and the edges are slightly inrolled. They are glabrous, dark green and glossy on the upper side, dull and light green on the underside, with a band of light spots along the main nerve. The main nerve and the apex usually terminate in single-celled hairs. The unisexual, regular flowers (1) grow in axil tufts. In the centre there is a male flower with the female ones around it. The perianth is yellowish-green. The stamens bear yellow anthers. The pistils have styles in threes, with large double-pronged stigmas. The fruits are triangular capsules.

● Box is native to the Mediterranean and extends as far as the southern part of the Alps. It is occasionally found growing wild in other parts of Europe. It is frequently grown as an evergreen ornamental shrub in parks, cemeteries and gardens. It flowers in March and April and is an important melliferous plant, producing an abundance of pollen.

It is easy to propagate both from seed and from cuttings. The basal twigs touching the ground take root easily. It tolerates cutting, regenerating afterwards in a compact growth. It flourishes best in semi-shade in soils rich in cal-cium and tolerates drought well. All parts of the plant are poisonous. The symptoms of poisoning are vomiting, colic pains, diarrhoea, breathing problems, and cramps in the final stage. It should never be used for home medicines.

In the past both the dried leaves and the wood were used for treating gout, rheumatism, malaria, chronic skin complaints and syphilis, but because of the harmful side-effects and the availability of other more suitable medicines, the wood fell into disuse.

1

Calendula officinalis L.
Pot Marigold

VI–IX ✷

VI–IX 🌿

Compositae

● Pot Marigold is an annual plant, lasting even longer in warm regions. The root is spindle-shaped. The erect stem, 30–50 cm (12–20 in) tall, is usually branched, even at the bottom, angular, downy, and bears dense alternate leaves. The leaves are tapering ovals, without petioles, entire or sparsely toothed, and hairy. The flower heads have a flat scaleless receptacle and a double row of tapering bracts with bristly hairs, terminating in an awn. The flowers are usually orange or yolk yellow in colour, but ornamental garden varieties may even be lemon yellow or orange-red. They are shiny during drought and approximately twice the length of the bracts. The reddish-brown disc-florets have tubular, five-lobed corollas. The ray-florets, arranged in two to three rows, are strap-shaped, pistillate and have filamentous stigmas. The fruit is a concave, sickle-shaped, spiny, furrowed achene (2).

● Pot Marigold is native to the Mediterranean and is widely cultivated as an ornamental plant in variously coloured varieties. The variety with only ray-florets (1) is grown for medicinal purposes. Sow the seeds in March or April directly in a sunny location sheltered from the wind, 1–2 cm ($\frac{2}{5}$–$\frac{4}{5}$ in) deep in rows 30–40 cm (12–16 in) apart. Thin the seedlings to a distance of 25–30 cm (10–12 in) apart. It is necessary to hoe and weed the bed two to three times.

The active constituents are in the entire flower heads or the ray-florets only. In popular healing, the haulm is also used. The plant flowers from July to September, but the largest quantities can be collected in August. Collect the flowers in dry, sunny weather, ideally about midday. Dry them as quickly as possible in the shade at a temperature of up to 35 °C (95 °F). Store in well-sealed containers.

An extract of dried flowers prepared with boiling water can be used to treat gallbladder disorders, inflammation of the bladder or ureter and gynaecological disorders. It may also be used as a gargle or mouth rinse and for compresses on inflamed skin and skin infections caused by microscopic fungi. The fresh haulm may be placed directly on skin inflammations and used for softening hard skin, and treating warts and corns. The juice is also used as a cosmetic.

1

2

Extract for menstrual disorders and for improving gallbladder activity: infuse 10 ml (2 teaspoons) dried flowers in 500 ml (18 fl oz) water. Take during the day.

Compress for refining the skin: mix 5–10 ml (1–2 teaspoons) juice from the fresh haulm with 250 ml (9 fl oz) milk.

Calluna vulgaris (L.) HULL.
Heather or Ling

Ericaceae

● This small shrub is 30–80 cm (12–31 in) in height. It is richly branched and the lower branches often grow along the ground, tending to take root; they are ascending at the ends. The leaves are alternate, dense, triangular and tough, resembling needles, with inrolled ends that almost grow together. They form a roof-shaped cover in four rows on the short, lateral twigs. They have no petioles and, at the base, have two small, spur-like ears. The branches terminate in solitary racemes of bright violet-pink (rarely white) flowers (1), which grow on short stalks in the axils of bracts. The green epicalyx is composed of four bracts, and the violet-pink calyx of four glossy petals. The calyx encloses a bell-shaped corolla, which is half the length of the calyx and divided into four lobes. There are eight stamens with pink filaments broadening into a club shape at the base, and several orange anthers. The fruit is a capsule with numerous brown seeds.

● Heather grows on sandy soils, on rocks, in open woodland and on moorland. It flourishes on acid soil. It is found on lowlands and uplands, where it often forms extensive cover. It flowers from the end of July to October. It is an important melliferous plant.

Plants growing in the wild can be collected, as it is very common. Cut off the haulm during flowering period, or snip about halfway along the twigs with garden scissors. Dry spread out in thin layers in the shade. Do not use artificial heat, as Heather loses its efficacy. It is also damaged by long-term storage, so use well-sealed containers.

Apart from having diuretic and disinfectant properties, it also stimulates the appetite and promotes digestion. Although it has an astringently bitter taste, a tasty drink can be made from it by mixing it with other medicinal herbs, such as Agrimony, Sage and Equisetum.

Larger doses are mildly narcotic, so it may be used to treat insomnia, nervous disorders, rheumatic pain and gout. Its main use is to treat inflammation of the kidneys or bladder and other disorders of the urinary system, and a lack of adequate gastric juices.

1

Drink with tranquillizing effects: infuse 10–15 g ($\frac{2}{3}$–$\frac{1}{2}$ oz) dried haulm in 400 ml (14 fl oz) boiling water or boil together for a very short time. The warm or cold drink should be taken in four doses during the day.

Capsella bursa-pastoris (L.) MEDIC.
Shepherd's Purse

Cruciferae

● This is an annual or biennial plant up to 60 cm (2 ft) in height. The root is simple or only slightly branched, yellowish-brown and somewhat woody. A rosette of basal leaves (1) grows first. This may either survive the winter or produce several flowering stems in the same year. The basal leaves are long and tapering, pinnately compound, lobed to entire and narrowing towards the stalk. The stem leaves have no petioles. They are enclosing, glabrous, and sparsely hairy along the nerves only. The main stem is erect, the others ascending and terminating in racemes of regular, tiny bisexual flowers. The inflorescence is at first clustered, later elongated. The calyx consists of four oval, bowl-shaped open green sepals, the corolla of four oblong, white petals which are twice as long as the calyx (2). Sometimes, however, it is stunted or not developed at all. There are six stamens with yellow anthers. The fruits are flat, heart-shaped pods with numerous small, oval, brown seeds.

● Shepherd's Purse is a common weed in gardens and fields. It also occurs on uncultivated land, dumping grounds, and in hedgerows. It flowers from March through to November.

The flowering haulm has medicinal properties. Collect it from spring to autumn and dry it spread out in thin layers in the shade in natural heat.

Haemostatic remedies are produced from it for medicinal purposes. In popular healing, it is used both internally and externally. A teaspoon of the juice from the fresh haulm may be taken five times a day for diarrhoea. A decoction, taken in several doses during the day, can help bleeding haemorrhoids. Make this from 10 g ($\frac{2}{5}$ oz) dried haulm in 400 ml (14 fl oz) dry wine. Biliousness may be helped by a decoction made from 10 g ($\frac{2}{5}$ oz) dried haulm in 500 ml (18 fl oz) water boiled for five minutes. Drink in doses of 5 ml (1 teaspoon) during the day. The freshly crushed haulm, soaked for 24 hours in vinegar, may be placed as a cooling compress on inflamed skin. Ointment to soothe inflamed skin can be made from 2 parts lard to 1 part fresh haulm or alcohol extract. Shepherd's Purse is also combined with other plants, such as birch leaves, in diuretic teas.

Extract (recommended by the Polish pharmacopoeia) for nose bleeds: infuse 15 ml (1 tablespoon) dried haulm in 200 ml (7 fl oz) hot water. Take in two or three doses during the day.

Carlina acaulis L.
Stemless Carline Thistle

Compositae

● This perennial plant has either a basal rosette of leaves and a completely stunted stem, or a stem up to 40 cm (16 in) in height, usually unbranched and densely leafy. It grows from a thick, spindle-shaped, perpendicular, bitter root that turns woody (1). The leaves in the basal rosette are slightly wavy, up to 30 cm (12 in) long and 6 cm (2$\frac{1}{4}$ in) wide. They are pinnately lobed and unequally spiny, tough and coloured light green. A single, large flower head, with a diameter of 5–15 cm (2–6 in) grows in the centre of the rosette or at the tip of the leafy stem. In some regions, however, the subspecies *caulescens* grows. This has branched stalks and a larger number of flower heads. The outer bracts are green, the inner ones brown with ridged spines. The inner circle is formed by narrow, long, white inwardly turned bracts resembling strap-shaped florets. They are pointed at the tip, coloured brownish in the lower parts and yellowish on the underside. The conical fleshy receptacle exudes a white milky substance when cut. The tubular flowers are a dingy white or pink and mature into achenes with feather-like fringed down at the tip (2).

● Stemless Carline Thistle grows on dry meadows, pastures, ridges, shrubby slopes and dry woodland clearings on lowlands and uplands. It flowers in August and September. The fleshy receptacle is sometimes eaten raw as a vegetable.

The young roots have medicinal properties. Clean them and then dry in moderate heat. They have a bitter, burning taste. Stemless Carline Thistle was widely used as a medicinal plant in the past and was cultivated in abundance in monastery gardens. It was used to treat roundworms and, in some places, a powder made from the root was smoked to alleviate toothache. The powdered root was sprinkled on scabies and other skin complaints, such as abscesses, cuts and scratches. A cosmetic decoction was made from the powdered root, vinegar and water. A decoction was prepared from the drug mixed with red wine to treat chills and reduce fever. Nowadays, Carline Thistle is used mainly in veterinary medicines, but it is still popular in some places as a diuretic for treating dropsy and disorders of the digestive system, as a fever-reducing agent and, sometimes, even as a cosmetic preparation for cleansing the skin. It has laxative properties and, in larger quantities, causes vomiting.

Diuretic tea: mix 25 g ($\frac{9}{10}$ oz) dried roots with 250 ml (9 fl oz) water and boil for five minutes. Allow to infuse and take in two doses, morning and evening.

Carum carvi L.
Caraway

Umbelliferae

V–VII

● Caraway is a carrot-like, biennial plant 50–80 cm (20–31 in) in height. In the first year, a rosette of basal leaves grows from the spindle-shaped root. The leaves are long, pinnately three times divided into fine filaments, with the petiole broadened into a membra- nous, furrowed sheath at the base. In the second year, a sparsely branched, fur- rowed, angular stem grows from the basal rosette. It has alternate leaves, which are stalked in the lower part and sessile with a membranous sheath in the upper part. The branches are termi- nated by compound umbels of flowers with 8–16 rays without covers. The rich umbels have one to three deciduous bracts. The calyx is stunted and has five inconspicuous small teeth. The corolla is formed of five white petals, which are often reddish when young, rarely per- manently pink, and deeply indented at the tip (1). The flowers on the periphery of the small umbels are usually longer, thus sometimes forming a ray. The five stamens grow alternately among the petals. The fruits are oval double achenes (2), narrowing towards each end, and concavely sickle-shaped, fur- rowed on the dorsal side and brown after maturing.

● Caraway grows in meadows, pas- tures, ridges, hedgerows and in grassy places in sparse, open woodland. It flourishes on both lowlands and up- lands. It is commonly cultivated as a spice. It flowers from May to July. Although it is not very demanding on the soil type, the best crops are from deep, heavy but not too damp soils sufficiently supplied with nutrients and humus.

Sow before the end of April in rows 40–50 cm (16–20 in) apart and at a depth of $1-2\frac{1}{2}$ cm ($\frac{2}{5}-1$ in). It germinates within two to four weeks. After germination, aerate the soil and weed the beds three or four times. Turn the soil again in the second year and weed again if necessary. Collect the fruits when they are turning brown and beginning to mature. Cut off the umbels from June to August, when two-thirds of the fruits have already matured. Leave them to dry through, thresh, clean and then sort them out. Store in well-sealed containers.

The fruits are used in the manufacture of liqueurs and in a variety of medicinal preparations. A Polish pharmacopoeia recommends a decoction made from Caraway to promote lactation in nursing mothers. The active constituents, passed on in the milk, also have a bene- ficial effect on the baby as a carminative – that is relieving flatulence. Caraway is also recommended for stimulating the appetite and digestion, for encouraging the formation of gall, for relieving cramp, and as a diuretic.

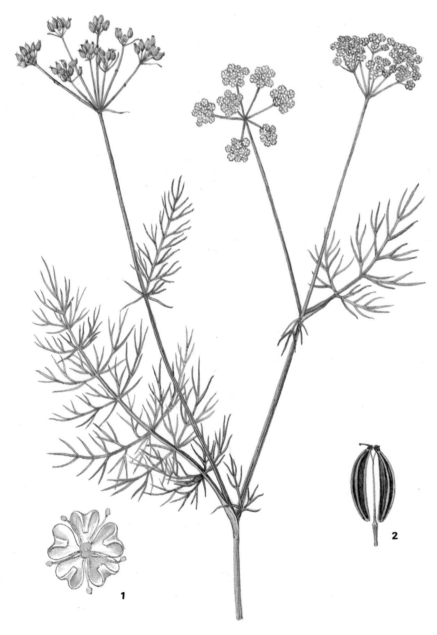

54

Centaurea cyanus L.
Cornflower

Compositae

● This is an annual plant. The taproot is spindle-shaped. The stem is erect, angular, 10–50 cm (4–20 in) tall and usually branched. The alternate leaves are slightly woolly when young and glabrous later. The basal leaves, narrowing into the petiole, are tapering or pinnately divided into several segments. The tapering stem leaves have no petioles. The upper ones are almost fibre-like and entire. The tips of stem branches bear individual flower heads. The oval bracts grow together and overlap. They are green, often with a violet tinge, and black at the tip. The tubular florets, coloured blue or, rarely, white, pink or violet, are large on the periphery, forming a prominent ray. The central florets are substantially shorter and predominantly violet. The outer florets are bisexual, the inner ones only pistillate. The fruits mature into long achenes with fine silky hairs on the surface. They are bluish-grey with white bands and have yellowish down at the tip.

● The Cornflower, a native of the eastern Mediterranean, flowers from June to August. It was once a very common weed in corn and potato fields, sometimes even growing in hedgerows and on hillsides. It has largely been destroyed in cultivated fields by modern farming techniques, but survives in some places such as areas where farming is still carried out on a small scale. Some coloured forms are cultivated in gardens as ornamental annuals.

The active constituents are in the large tubular florets. Dry them very quickly in the shade. They must retain their original colour.

Formerly Cornflower was used for the manufacture of a blue dye, in the preparation of perfumes and as a spice. In popular healing, a decoction made from the blossoms was taken for jaundice and conjunctivitis. Nowadays, it is used mainly as a diuretic and anti-inflammatory medicine. It also promotes the production of bile. Its exceptional diuretic effects have been confirmed in Poland by specific clinical cases in which patients who were treated with a decoction made from the flowers were able to excrete double the usual quantity of urine. These effects have also been verified by experiments on rats. The decoction can also be used to bathe wounds and abscesses.

Diuretic tea from the Polish pharmacopoeia: infuse 10 g (⅖ oz) dried flowers in 250 ml (9 fl oz) boiling water. Take in three doses, between meals, during the day.

Centaurium erythraea RAFN.
Common Centaury

Gentianaceae

● This annual or biennial plant grows to a height of 50 cm (20 in). The short root produces a network of slender, intertwined rootlets and a rosette of basal leaves, which, in some cases, survives the winter. The basal leaves are oval, rounded at the ends and narrowing towards the petiole. They usually have five veins. The erect, green, square stem is usually richly branched in the upper part. The stem leaves are opposite and have no petioles. They are oval and tapering and entire. The bisexual, regular flowers grow in dense, flat clusters. They have a tubular calyx divided into five narrow, tapering lobes with long points at the tip. The pink corolla is divided into five flatly spreading tips. Attached to the corolla are five stamens, the anthers of which twist after releasing pollen. The pistil has a filamented style with two stigmas. The fruit matures into a narrow, cylindrical capsule with two cells containing many tiny brown seeds.

● Common Centaury grows in clearings, open woodland, in pastures and in sparse hedgerows. It does well in mineral-rich soil. It flowers in July and August.

The whole haulm is collected when in flower. Cut off the stem tips with the inflorescence, leaving the lower part where it is. Do not pull up the whole plant, as this decreases the quality of the active constituents, besides destroying the plant unnecessarily. The remainder of the growing stem will produce new branches from the leaf axils and flower again to a second crop, which is often richer in medicinal properties. Dry the haulms in small bundles or laid out on shelves in moderate heat – maximum 40 °C (104 °F). Do not turn them too often. The flowers, leaves and stalks should retain the fresh colour.

Digestifs are manufactured from Common Centaury and teas may also be helpful for digestive disorders and loss of appetite. In popular healing, an extract made from the drug is also used as a cosmetic preparation for unhealthy skin. The decoction is very bitter to the taste and should not be sweetened.

Extract for loss of appetite and stomach disorders: scald 5 ml (1 teaspoon) pulverized, dried haulm with 500 ml (18 fl oz) hot water and leave to macerate for 10 minutes. Take in small sips during the day. The powdered haulm may also be used for the same purposes – a small pinch three times a day.

Chamaemelum nobile (L.) ALL.
Chamomile

Compositae

● This is a perennial plant, the stems of which grow to a height of up to 30 cm (12 in). The rhizome grows quite deep in the ground and is richly branched. Numerous small roots grow vertically into the ground. There may be numerous stems growing along the ground or there may be erect, simple or sparsely branched stems. The stems take root readily, so that the plant forms dense, extensive growths. The leaves are alternate and bipinnate, with the narrow sections pointed at the ends. Depending on the habitat, the leaves are densely or sparsely hairy, greyish-green or a deep green. The stems and branches bear individual stalked flower heads at their tips. The oval bracts have dry, membranous edges. In wild plants (1), the flower heads are composed of two types of florets: the white, strap-shaped ray-florets, which are longer than the inwardly turned bracts and divided at the end into three uneven, small teeth, and the tubular disc-florets which are bisexual and yellow. Varieties with only strap-shaped florets are mainly cultivated for medicinal purposes. The fruits are triangular, glabrous and glossy achenes.

● Chamomile is native to southern Europe. It grows in pastures, in sandy, gravelly deposits, near water and also in dry locations. However, excessive moisture damages it and it is unable to tolerate permanent damp. It flowers in July and August, in warm positions as early as June. Since the 16th century, it has been cultivated in gardens in central Europe mainly in the double-flowered form with only the strap-shaped florets. It is propagated mainly by dividing clumps in March and April. The young plants are planted at a distance 50 cm (20 in) apart and spread into a rich cover. The plants are left for three to four years. In cooler regions during a hard winter, the plants should be protected from frost. When propagated from seed, the second generation is very variable.

The flowers contain the active constituents. Collect the flowering inflorescence without the stalks. It should not be squashed. Dry it immediately in the shade at a temperature of about 35 °C (95 °F). It must not turn brown while drying. It very readily absorbs atmospheric moisture, and should, therefore, be stored in well-sealed containers. An essence is distilled from the flower heads for cosmetic purposes.

It is used in a similar way to Common Chamomile, although its anti-inflammatory and disinfectant properties are weaker. Chamomile regulates digestion and relieves cramp. An extract is taken internally for cramp in smooth muscle, painful menstruation, and for uterine, gastric and intestinal cramp. It has tranquillizing effects on the nervous system. It may also be used as a gargle or for bathing inflamed skin.

1

Chamomilla recutita (L.) Rauschert
Scented Mayweed, Wild Chamomile

V–IX ❀

Compositae

This annual is a pleasantly aromatic plant. Growing from the slender taproot is an erect, 30–50 cm (12–20 in) high, richly branched, glabrous stem. The leaves are alternate and two or three times odd-pinnately divided, having flat, glabrous, narrow sections. The single flower heads, opening at the tips of the branches, close for the night. These have a single row of blunt bracts with a membranous margin. The receptacle is conically arched, hollow and glabrous (1). On the periphery of the flower head, there is a ray of about 15 white strap-shaped, downward bending florets. They are oval and indented at the tips into three small teeth. The golden yellow disc is formed of tubular bisexual florets with a five-toothed corolla. Each floret contains five stamens, the anthers of which are fused to form a tube. Among them is the style of the pistil, terminating in two stigmas. The fruits are small, downless achenes.

Scented Mayweed grows in warmer regions as a weed in cornfields and among root-crops, in hedgerows, on unused land and dumping grounds. It flowers from June to September.

Collect the flower heads with no more than 2 cm ($\frac{3}{4}$ in) of the stalks, from May to September in dry weather around midday. They should be collected before reaching full bloom, otherwise they will fall apart while being dried. Collect them carefully in baskets without squashing them, and start to dry them within three hours. Dry them as carefully as possible in the shade without turning. The flowers are mostly obtained from cultivated plants and dried in large quantities by artificial heat at temperatures up to 40 °C (104 °F). The flowers must retain their aroma and colour, and should not fall apart.

For cultivation light sandy-loamy soils containing sufficient calcium are best. Choose a warm, sunny site sheltered from the wind and excessive drying out. Sow the seeds in spring or autumn, in rows 30 cm (12 in) apart, on the surface of the soil. They germinate within about two weeks.

Both the extract and the decoction made from Scented Mayweed have antibacterial properties, so that they may be used both internally and externally for inflammatory conditions and in cosmetics. Scented Mayweed also has astringent properties, helps to reduce fever, is suitable for treating cramp caused by flatulence and asthma in children.

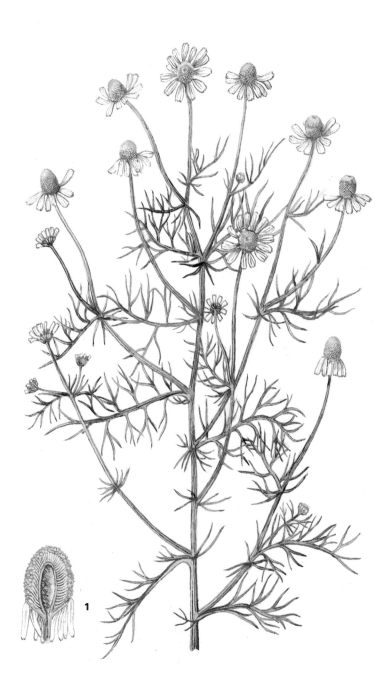

Fever-reducing tea (also used for treating sore throats, gastric problems and flatulence): scald 10 g ($\frac{2}{5}$ oz) dried flowers with 250 ml (9 fl oz) boiling water. Drink while very hot.

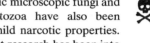

Chelidonium majus L.
Greater Celandine

Papaveraceae

● This is a perennial, poisonous plant with an unpleasant smell. It grows to a height of 1 m (39 in). The rhizome is cylindrical and branched into several heads bearing rosettes of basal leaves. It is reddish-brown on the surface and yellow inside, exuding an orange milky substance. It produces numerous slender, vivid orange to reddish-brown rootlets. The basal leaves are numerous, clustered, long-stalked, pinnately lobed with five sections on each side, light green, dull and glabrous on the upper side and bluish-green and sparsely hairy below. From the basal rosettes, richly branched, bluntly angular, hollow, woolly stems grow early in spring. They are swollen in the places where they branch. The stem leaves are alternate, either without petioles or short-stalked, pinnately lobed with two to three sections on each side. The sections are oval, toothed at the edges and rounded at the tips. Sparse umbels of regular yellow flowers on long stalks grow from the leaf axils. The two sepals fall early. There are four oval petals and a larger number of stamens. The fruit is a long, green capsule.

● Greater Celandine is distributed throughout the whole of Europe and is especially abundant in lowlands. It occurs on hills only as an escape around human settlements or on wasteland. It flowers from May to September. The entire plant exudes an orange sap, which is poisonous, has an unpleasant smell and a sharp, bitter taste. It irritates the mucous membranes and some people's skin. The oily, glossy black seeds have a colourless, gelatinous protuberance, attractive to ants, which, therefore, help to propagate the plant.

The plant is only used by commercial pharmaceutical companies. The whole haulm is collected in spring when it contains the maximum quantity of active constituents, or the rhizomes are collected in autumn. The plants are then dried.

Greater Celandine is poisonous and should not be used for home medicines.

The pharmaceutical industry uses it in the manufacture of tranquillizers and medicines for relieving cramp, for promoting the production of the bile and for checking the reproduction of bacteria. Its properties in combating some pathogenic microscopic fungi and parasitical protozoa have also been noted. It has mild narcotic properties. The most recent research has been into its effects in checking the growth of tumour cells.

59

Cichorium intybus L.
Chicory

Compositae

● Chicory is a perennial herb growing up to 150 cm (59 in) in height. The root is cylindrical to spindle-shaped (long and branched in wild plants) (1). When cut, a white milky substance with a bitter taste flows from it. In the cultivated variety (*C. i. sativum*) the root is large and fleshy and can weigh more than 500 g (18 oz). The root produces a rosette of basal leaves with winged petioles. These leaves later dry out. Richly branched, tough, furrowed, angular, glabrous or hairy stems grow from the rosette. The stem leaves are alternate and without petioles. The lower ones are lobed, and hairy on the underside, the upper ones elongated to tapering, partly enclosing the stem. Numerous flower heads with a double row of bracts grow from the axils of the leaves. The bracts have bristly hairs and glands, the outer ones being shorter, oval and spreading, the inner ones tapering and erect. There are only strap-shaped florets (2) in the heads, coloured blue, more rarely white or pink. They are bisexual. The fruits are oval, bristly achenes with five ribs.

● Chicory grows predominantly on lowland pastures, meadows, hedgerows, embankments, wasteland and dumping grounds. It flowers from July to September. The flower heads close in bad weather, before rain and in the afternoon. Chicory can be cultivated on deep loamy or sandy-loamy soils.

Collect the haulm from July to September in the afternoon. Pull the inflorescence and leaves off the stem and dry spread out in thin layers in the shade. Dig up the roots in September and October. Wash and dry them for one or two weeks in a single layer in the shade. Complete the drying process with artificial heat at temperatures up to 50 °C (122 °F) until they lose their elasticity and are easily broken.

An extract made from the root with boiling water may be taken for loss of appetite, gastric problems, jaundice and liver complaints. It affects the metabolism and the activity of the gallbladder. An extract made from the haulm slightly stimulates the excretion of bile. Fresh haulm may also be placed on painful, inflamed skin. An extract made from the haulm in alcohol is used for massage after a lengthy confinement in bed and other immobility to help regenerate muscles. Inulin is isolated from the root for medicinal purposes.

> **Extract with mild effects on bile excretion:** infuse 5 ml (1 teaspoon) dried, chopped root in 200 ml (7 fl oz) boiling water. Take three times daily.

Colchicum autumnale L.
Meadow Saffron

Liliaceae

● This is a poisonous perennial plant. In many countries, it is protected. It has an oval, 3–6 cm (1–2 ¼) high corm covered with brown, undivided scales. At the end of the summer, one to three light violet-pink flowers grow from it. They have a long, whitish tube which extends into a bell shape in the upper part, consisting of six oval, tapering petals which are downy inside. Six stamens, with filaments shorter than the orange-yellow anthers, grow from the mouth of the perianth tube. From the superior ovary, situated deep in the ground, three styles grow, terminating in elongated to club-shaped stigmas. The ovary is formed of three carpels. The following spring tapering, entire basal leaves grow from the corm. Among these grow one to three oval light green capsules divided into three cells with a remnant of the dried stigmas at the top. These contain a large number of blackish-brown, spherical seeds.

● Meadow Saffron grows in damp meadows, wet woods, especially in alder groves, on lowlands and uplands. The number of its habitats is diminishing and it is, therefore, a protected species in many countries.

It can be propagated from seeds and corms and is cultivated as an ornamental plant on rockeries. Sow the seed in September in a cold frame. It germinates in winter or spring. Plant out in August of the second year into damp soil, 8 cm (3 in) deep and 7–15 cm (2 ¾–6 in) apart.

The daughter corms can be used for further propagation. Plant in July and August in the same way as the seedlings.

The mature seeds contain the active constituents. Occasionally the corms are also used. The almost fully mature, brown capsules are cut off in June and July and thoroughly dried before the seeds are beaten out of them. The corms are dug up in August and September.

As Meadow Saffron is poisonous, it should never be used for home medicines. Medicines for treating inflammation of the joints, severe cases of gout and rheumatism, and even pernicious anaemia, are manufactured commercially.

Convallaria majalis L.
Lily-of-the-Valley

Liliaceae

 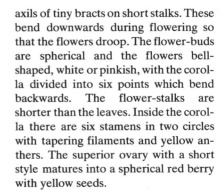

Lily-of-the-Valley had long been used as a medicinal plant. It has a creeping, richly branched, pointed rhizome. At the ends of its branches, spindle-like buds grow. Two or three basal leaves grow from the buds, and, from the convex ones, a flowering stem also grows. The leaves are tapering, glabrous, entire, pointed and with long petioles, which are covered in the lower part with pink to brown scales. A leafless flowering stalk grows beside the petiole. The flowers, arranged in a sparse, single raceme, grow from the axils of tiny bracts on short stalks. These bend downwards during flowering so that the flowers droop. The flower-buds are spherical and the flowers bell-shaped, white or pinkish, with the corolla divided into six points which bend backwards. The flower-stalks are shorter than the leaves. Inside the corolla there are six stamens in two circles with tapering filaments and yellow anthers. The superior ovary with a short style matures into a spherical red berry with yellow seeds.

Lily-of-the-Valley grows in open deciduous woods and, less often, in coniferous forests, hedgerows, and sometimes even outside woods in meadows. It flourishes on lowlands and highlands. It is cultivated in gardens as an ornamental plant and flowers in May and June.

The flowering haulm, leaves and flowers contain the active constituents. Cut off the haulm close to the ground and remove any dry leaf remnants or adhering grass. Dry in the shade, in thin layers, without turning, or hung in bundles. The flowers are most frequently pulled off the stalks on the spot and dried in the shade. The leaves must be well-developed, dark green, undamaged and without stalks. Dry them in the shade in thin layers.

Lily-of-the-Valley is propagated from the buds together with part of the rhizome and small roots. Plant in damp soil 20 cm (8 in) apart in rows 10 cm (4 in) apart. Water and cover with leaves or compost. If the plants are to be grown from seed, crush the mature berries and soak them in water. Rinse and dry the seeds. Sow from April onwards directly in position in damp, humus-rich soil, in semi-shade.

Medicines for regulating heart activity are manufactured from Lily-of-the-Valley by the pharmaceutical industry. The plant also forms part of diuretic medicines. It is also used in the manufacture of perfumes. In the past, mainly in the 15th century, it was widely used in popular healing, when it formed part of every herbarium. As Lily-of-the-Valley is poisonous, it should never be used for home medicines.

III−V

 VI−VII

 IX

Corylus avellana L.
Hazel

Betulaceae

● Hazel is an undemanding shrub, rarely a tree, 3−6 m (10−20 ft) in height. It has brown to red bark which is smooth, even when old. The shoots are greyish-yellow and densely bristled, and older twigs are dark brown. The oval or round buds are alternate and in two rows, slightly flattened, rounded at the ends and covered with four to six yellowish to greenish-brown scales. The leaves are alternate and round, with heart-shaped indentations at the petioles. They are pointed at the ends. The margins have long and short teeth. The blade is downy on the underside; the petiole is covered with small hairs. The male flowers bloom in drooping catkins on the twigs of the previous year (1). In the scale axils, there are two large bracts and four stamens. The female flowers grow at the ends of the current year's twigs and resemble buds (2). Pistils with two red stigmas protruding from the scales are located in the axils of the pointed, oval bracts. The fruits are oval nuts (3) with a hard, brown, smooth shell surrounded by pointed green bracts.

● Hazel grows on uplands throughout almost the whole of Europe in open woodland, at the edges of woods and on rocky slopes. Sometimes, it is found at elevations of over 1,000 m (3,300 ft) above sea level. It has a marked resistance to drought and is often cultivated as a shrub in gardens.

The leaves and the oily nuts contain many valuable mineral constituents. Oil is pressed from them. Collect the leaves in June and July and dry them quickly, spread out in a thin layer. The temperature should not exceed 40 °C (104 °F). Occasionally, people collect the bark in the spring months and dry it in the same way either by natural or artificial heat.

Hazel leaves contain constituents which relieve cramp in the digestive tract, flatulence and diarrhoea. Tea made from the leaves has mild diuretic properties. An extract made from the leaves may be applied to suppurating wounds, haemorrhoids and varicose veins. Similar curative properties are attributed to the bark. The nuts are used

mainly in the food industry. Crushed seeds mixed with honey may be taken for coughs. In Yugoslavia, extracts and ointments are prepared from the leaves and bark to treat inflammations of the veins, varicose veins, and as haemostatics. A decoction made from the leaves

is taken for excessive menstrual bleeding. In Romania, an extract made from the bark and leaves is used for herpes, ringworm and eczema. An extract of crushed hazel nuts, fresh yeast and alcohol, mixed with olive oil, may be placed as a compress on wounds.

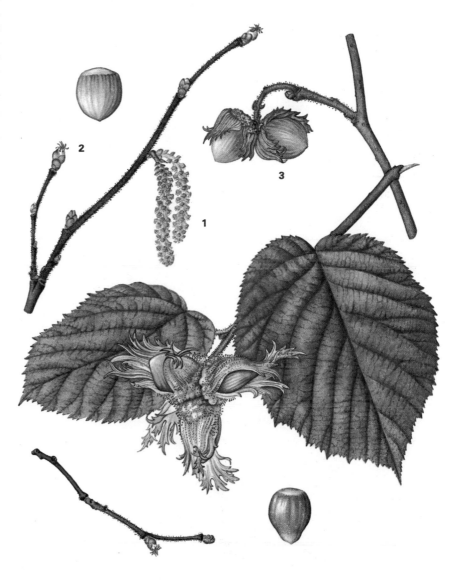

Crataegus monogyna JACQ.
Hawthorn

Rosaceae

V–VI
V–VI
VI–IX

● This thorny shrub or tree, 3–5 m (10–16 ft) tall, has grey bark which cracks into plates when older. The shoots are green to light brown; the older twigs are ash grey. The lateral twigs often terminate in a thorn. The buds are alternate and arranged in a spiral, and are angularly globular, black and glossy. Straight thorns usually grow under the lateral buds. The leaves are alternate, oval and deeply pinnately divided on either side into three to five lobes, which are toothed at the ends and entire between the lobes. The short petioles grow from the axil of two deciduous stipules. The flowers grow in clusters. The small sepals are pointed and the petals are round, white or pink in colour. There are about 20 stamens. The pistil generally has only one style, terminating in a club-shaped stigma. The fruit is light red, and round or oval, usually containing only one stone with two furrows along the sides and a seam on the crown. The flesh of the fruit is floury.

● Hawthorn grows in light, sparse woods, mainly on the edges, in pastures, in hedgerows and on rocky slopes on lowlands and uplands.

The flowers, the whole inflorescence, including the young leaves, leaves and fruits, contain the active ingredients. Collect them during flowering in May or June; collect the fruits in full maturity in September (in some places as early as the end of August). Dry them as quickly as possible, spread out in thin layers in the shade. The flowers should not be turned and the temperature must not exceed 40 °C (104 °F). The dried flowers are white or yellowish. The fruits are best dried with artificial heat. Alternatively, dry them in a thin layer in a warm room and complete the process at a temperature of up to 70 °C (158 °F). Store in bags in a dry, airy place and check, from time to time, to make sure that they do not become mouldy or damp.

Hawthorn is used in the pharmaceutical industry for the manufacture of hypotensives and antisclerotics and is a constituent of some tranquillizers. In popular healing, it is recommended for stimulating heart activity and as a hypotensive. It has a beneficial effect after physical or mental strain, on insomnia, irritability, heart palpitations and nervousness and shortness of breath. It is best taken as an extract or tincture. It should not be used by patients taking some prescribed heart medicines because, in some instances, the two in combination can have seriously damaging or fatal effects. The fruits are diuretic and anti-spasmodic. People with heart conditions should not use Hawthorn as a home medicine.

Cucurbita pepo L.
Vegetable Marrow

Cucurbitaceae

● This annual plant has climbing stalks up to 5 m (16 ft) long or forms a small shrubby growth, about 50 cm (20 in) in height. A number of edible and ornamental varieties are cultivated. Several angular, coarsely bristled, juicy stems grow from the branched, dirty white root. The leaves are alternate and petioled, bristly, heart-shaped and lobed or to a greater or lesser extent deeply palmately indented into five points. In climbing varieties, branched tendrils grow beside the petioles. The flowers are unisexual. The male flowers grow either individually or, more often, in bunches, from the lower leaf axils. They have a five-pointed calyx and a large, bell-shaped corolla which is vivid yellow in colour and divided into five points. Inside there are five stamens fused into a small club-shaped column. The female flowers grow individually in the leaf axils, higher up on the plant than the male ones. The superior ovary matures into large yellow or green berries containing large, flat, oval seeds (1).

● Vegetable Marrow, probably originates from North or Central America. The fruits are eaten as a vegetable and used to make jam. Varieties with small fruits of various shapes and colours are cultivated as ornamental plants.

Cultivating ornamental and edible varieties together is not recommended, because some ornamental varieties have bitter flesh or other undesirable characteristics. They readily produce hybrids, which then have neither useful nor ornamental value. Vegetable Marrow is cultivated from seed. Sow in position during the second half of May, or earlier in a frame. It requires a humus-rich soil with sufficient nutrients and moisture. The shrubby varieties are planted at a distance of 1 m (39 in) apart; the creeping varieties at a distance of 2 m (79 in) apart.

The mature seeds are used to treat parasitic worms. In contrast with other drugs used for this purpose, they are not poisonous and have no undesirable side-effects. The flesh of the fruits has diuretic properties and may be beneficial in treating chronic inflammation of the kidneys. According to recent observations, Vegetable Marrow may be helpful in treating inflammation of the small intestine and psoriasis.

Seeds for treating parasitic worms: peel and crush 150–250 g (5–9 oz) seeds in water with fruit syrup. For children, use 30–100 g (1–4 oz) seeds. Take in two doses, half an hour apart, on an empty stomach. After two to three hours take 30 g (1 oz) castor oil. Children should take 10–15 g ($\frac{2}{5}-\frac{3}{5}$ oz). Repeat as required after two to three days.

1

65

Daphne mezereum L.
Mezereon

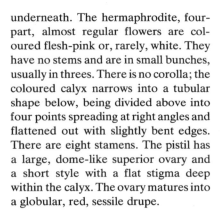

Thymelaeaceae

● This erect shrub, up to 150 cm (59 in) high, has smooth, greyish-brown bark. The shoots are erect, extremely flexible, firm, smooth and greyish-green. The older twigs are yellowish-brown to greyish-brown. The buds are alternate, arranged in a spiral, conical, bluntly tipped, brownish with dark red edges and with overlapping scale covers. The rounder blossom buds are in spike-like clusters slanting against one another. The leaves are alternate, tapering, being broadest in the upper half, and entire. The blade is greyish-blue underneath. The hermaphrodite, four-part, almost regular flowers are coloured flesh-pink or, rarely, white. They have no stems and are in small bunches, usually in threes. There is no corolla; the coloured calyx narrows into a tubular shape below, being divided above into four points spreading at right angles and flattened out with slightly bent edges. There are eight stamens. The pistil has a large, dome-like superior ovary and a short style with a flat stigma deep within the calyx. The ovary matures into a globular, red, sessile drupe.

● Mezereon flourishes in upland and lowland forests. It flowers before the leaves sprout in March and April. The whole plant is highly poisonous. In most countries it is a protected species and is cultivated as an ornamental plant in gardens.

The bark is collected for pharmaceutical purposes. It is peeled off the trunks in early spring and dried in bundles hanging in dry and airy places. It should not be handled except by professionals as, without proper protection, the skin can absorb the poison. Symptoms of poisoning are a burning sensation in the mouth, stomach pains, vomiting, diarrhoea and kidney inflammation with painful bleeding when urinating.

All parts of the plant contain the poison mezeraine and it should never be used for home medicines. In the past, it was used to treat a variety of conditions and its medicinal properties have been the subject of recent research.

VI–VII

VI–VIII

VII–IX

Datura stramonium L.
Thorn-apple

Solanaceae

● This is an annual herb 60–100 cm (24–39 in) in height. An erect, glabrous, broadly branched stem grows from the spindle-like root. The alternate, oval leaves, pointed at the ends, narrow towards the long petiole in a wedge shape. They are deeply lobed and toothed, up to 30 cm (12 in) long and 15 cm (6 in) wide, dark on the upper side and lighter green and glabrous on the underside. Three to five thicker lateral nerves run from the main nerve. The flowers grow singly at the places where the stem branches or at the ends of the branches. They are on short stalks and are bisexual. The calyx is tubular, five-toothed and five-sided. When the fruits mature its points fall. The corolla is white, long and funnel-shaped, folded before flowering, and divided into five sharply pointed lobes (1). There are five stamens of equal length. The superior ovary has a long style and a double-lobed stigma. The fruit is a prickly, oval capsule (2) which bursts open in five valves containing many black kidney-shaped seeds (3).

● Thorn-apple was introduced from Central America as an ornamental plant. Since then, it has spread over a substantial part of Europe, Asia and North America, where it grows on waste ground and other abandoned places, in hedgerows and on embankments. It flowers from June to September.

It is cultivated by the pharmaceutical industry for medicinal purposes. It tolerates even poor soil, although the highest yields and highest content of active substances are produced on healthy, calcareous, not too dry soils rich in nutrients. It requires a warm, sunny position.

The active constituents are found in the leaves and in the haulm with the whole root. The plant is very poisonous and should never be used for home medicines.

Thorn-apple is used to manufacture medicines to treat asthma, cramp, Parkinson's disease and other disorders of the nervous system. It is also used in anti-asthmatic cigarettes.

67

Daucus carota L.
Carrot

Umbelliferae

VI—VIII

VIII—IX

VII—IX

● The Carrot is a biennial herb 30—80 cm (12—31 in) high. The wild plants have a slender, spindle-shaped taproot which tends to turn woody; the cultivated varieties have a spindle-shaped or cylindrical, fleshy root coloured red or yellow (1). In the first year, a rosette of basal leaves forms and only exceptionally does a plant reach the flowering stage. The basal leaves are up to four times pinnately divided, triangular to oval, with pinnately lobed sections and coarsely uneven toothing. In the second year an erect stem grows from the root. This is simple or sparsely branched in the upper part, tough, bristly and coarsely furrowed on the surface. On rare occasions, at stream sources and in peat-bogs, almost glabrous plants occur. The stem leaves are alternate, the lower ones on short stalks, the upper ones without stalks but with a small sheath. Flat umbels of white, yellowish or pinkish flowers (2) grow at the tip of the stem and branches. In the centre of each umbel, there are usually one or several flowers coloured a dark violet. The small and large covers are composed of large, pinnately divided bracts. The fruits are oval achenes with protruding, bristled ribs (3).

● Carrot grows in meadows, along field paths, in open woodland, on rocky slopes, in coastal undergrowth and as a weed in gardens and fields. It flourishes on lowlands as well as uplands. Numerous cultivated varieties are grown as a vegetable and as fodder.

The fruits in wild plants and the roots in cultivated varieties have medicinal properties. Cut off the umbels with the fruits before they reach full maturity. Thresh and dry. The fresh leaves also have medicinal properties.

An extract made from the fruits is used as a diuretic to treat dropsy, diseases of the urinary tract and metabolic disorders. Anti-spasmodic effects have also been observed in this extract, especially in cases of long-term heart vasodilatation and incipient angina pectoris. Home treatment for these conditions is inadvisable. In popular healing, the roots are mainly used, as they are rich in vitamins A, B and C and in carotene. A decoction made from the root is a reliable preparation for treating diarrhoea in children. Finely grated root is given for liver complaints, jaundice, intestinal inflammation, exhaustion and during convalescence, regulating digestive disorders, especially in children, and malnutrition. The juice from the root is an auxiliary medicine for treating parasitic worms, and it also prevents night blindness. There is evidence of its efficacy in treating enlarged tonsils in children, and polyps. The fresh leaves may be placed on burns and crushed leaves on abscesses and suppurating wounds to aid healing. The Carrot, especially when eaten raw, is a highly significant, cheap source of vitamins, sugar, carotene and minerals in human nutrition.

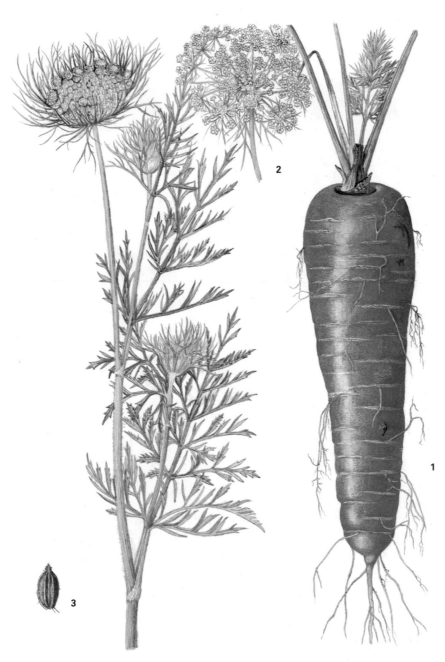

Delphinium consolida L.
Forking Larkspur

Ranunculaceae

VI–VIII
VI–VIII
IX

● Forking Larkspur is an annual herb. An erect stem, 40–100 cm (16–39 in) tall, grows from the short taproot (1). The stem is very richly branched and either covered with very short hair or glabrous. The leaves are alternate and up to three times palmately divided into long, narrowly linear sections. In the upper part of the stem the leaves are less divided or simple. The flowers grow on long stalks in sparse, often branched racemes, in the axils of short, narrow bracts. They are bluish-violet, rarely pink or white. The petals are fused and transformed into three-lobed nectaries. The five-part calyx, composed of oval sepals, is the same colour as the corolla. The flower extends into a narrowly conical, perpendicular or slantingly spreading spur, which is erect and slightly hairy. There are eight to ten stamens. The single, erect, cylindrical, glabrous pistil with a superior ovary narrows abruptly into a short stigma. The fruit is a follicle containing a substantial number of blackish-brown, rough seeds.

● Forking Larkspur is a field weed which is disappearing with the use of herbicides. In some places it has survived in fodder crops, such as in sparse clover fields. It also has a secondary distribution on dumping grounds, waste ground, in hedgerows and on dry rocky slopes.

Either the whole haulm or just the flowers may be collected from June to August. Collect the mature seeds in September. Pick the flowers or the plant tips at the places where the plant branches. Dry quickly in the shade. If you are using artificial heat, the temperature should not exceed 40 °C (104 °F).

Forking Larkspur is not now used in popular medicine, except under medical supervision. It has been used in popular healing as a diuretic and laxative, for gynaecological disorders and to prevent infestation with parasitic worms. It was added to anti-tussive teas, particularly for improving the appearance of tea blends. Tea made from the flowers was used to treat whooping cough and sometimes asthma. It was also added to various expectorant blends. An ointment made from crushed seeds was used to treat lice, scabies and occasionally other skin parasites. Sometimes the seeds were chewed to treat inflamed and infected gums. A dye for colouring confectionery and for dyeing silk was made from the flowers.

69

Digitalis purpurea L.
Foxglove

Scrophulariaceae

The Foxglove is a poisonous, perennial herb with stems 60–150 cm (24–59 in) tall. In the first year a rosette of basal leaves grows from the spindle-shaped, branched root. These are oval, narrowing at the base into a short, triangular, winged petiole. At the margin they are coarsely and unevenly toothed, on the underside grey-felted with pronounced, very dense veins. In the second year a stout, erect, unbranched, grey-felted leafy stem grows from the basal rosette, terminating in a rich single raceme of flowers. The stem leaves are alternate, becoming progressively smaller towards the top. At the top of the stem they have no petioles, have heart-shaped indentations, are slightly enclosing and bluntly tipped. They gradually change into bracts in the inflorescence. The short-stalked, drooping flowers have a calyx composed of five pointed oval lobes. The corolla is symmetrical, bell-shaped, shallowly divided at the margin into four to five lobes, hairy inside, and coloured pink to red or white with reddish-brown spots. The fruit is a hairy capsule containing many seeds in two cells (1).

The Foxglove is native to western Europe. It flourishes particularly well on calcium-free soil on lowlands and uplands. It is also cultivated as an ornamental plant in gardens. It flowers from June to August.

Sow the seed directly in position or in a frame, 5 mm ($\frac{1}{5}$ in) deep in rows 8–10 cm (3–4 in) apart. Prick out the seedlings.

The leaves from the basal rosettes are used in commercial medicines. They have a larger and more constant content of active substances than the stem leaves.

Foxglove is highly poisonous and very dangerous. It should never be used for home medicines. Medicines made from Foxglove are produced by the pharmaceutical industry for regulating heart activity in some types of heart disease.

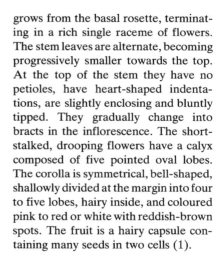

Drosera rotundifolia L.
Round-leaved Sundew

Droseraceae

● This insectivorous plant is a low perennial. It has a very short rhizome with fibrillous rootlets. Growing from this is a basal rosette of long-stalked leaves with round, spoon-shaped blades which are glabrous on the underside. On the upper side and at the edges they are covered with long, red glandular hairs which exude a sticky liquid, to which small insects adhere. The plant digests their soft parts with the liquid. A slender, glossy, leafless stalk terminates in a sparse spike of small flowers and buds on short stalks. The flowers open successively from the bottom upwards and fade quickly, so that there are only one or two open flowers on the plant at a time.

The calyx is deeply divided into five points. There are five white petals and five stamens. The pistil is divided into three filaments and three club-shaped stigmas. The one-celled ovary develops into a smooth, oval capsule containing a large number of small brown seeds.

● Round-leaved Sundew grows in peat-bogs, near springs or on permanently wet acid meadows, sometimes spreading to the immediate surroundings. It cannot tolerate an alkaline environment. The plant flowers in June and July, as late as August in higher, harsher localities. It is a rare and protected species, and is constantly declining in numbers in the natural environment as a result of the drainage of meadows, the exploitation of peat-bogs, the calcification of meadows and ponds, the pollution of water with industrial fertilizers, and the overgrowth of protected sites with woodland or dense rush and sedge cover. Wild plants may not be collected. Round-leaved Sundew can be cultivated on suitably prepared, suffi-ciently damp ground by sowing it directly into peat mixed with sand.

Harvest the whole haulm during the flowering period. Remove any remnants of moss and grass and dry the haulm in thin layers in the shade. Store in well-sealed containers.

An extract made from the haulm has diuretic properties and is used to check arteriosclerosis and for relieving spasms in asthma and whooping cough. It helps to loosen phlegm and encourages expectoration.

> **Extract for respiratory disorders:** scald 2 g ($\frac{1}{10}$ oz) dried haulm with 500 ml (18 fl oz) boiling water. Take during the day.

Dryopteris filix-mas (L.) Schott.
Male Fern

Aspidiaceae

● This perennial herb has a stout brown rhizome in the ground, usually ascending at an angle and densely covered with scales (3). It is oval in cross-section and coloured bright green. Its tissue is soft and spongy. The apex of the rhizome produces a rosette of leaves arranged in a funnel, which have thick scaly stalks. When young the leaves are coiled in a spiral, straightening up progressively from the base. They are tapering, dark green, and simply pinnately divided. The individual leaflets are feathery and toothed at the edges. The main rib is tough, and covered, like the stalk, with rust-coloured glumes. The blade is a lighter green on the underside and two rows of sporangia (1) appear on it from June to September. These are round and covered with quite thick kidney-shaped perisporangia which are greyish when young and later reddish brown (2).

● Male Fern grows quite abundantly in shady places in woods, on rocks, in hedges and clearings and, to a lesser extent, on old walls. It is also cultivated as an ornamental plant in gardens.

It is propagated from the spores. Either place the leaves with the mature spores directly in position or sprinkle the spores on a piece of paper and then sow them in a mixture of well-matured compost and forest litter. Sterilize the compost with boiling water or by heating it to 100 °C (212 °F) before sowing the spores. Cover the pots with glass and leave in a shady place. Water the drip trays, not the surface of the compost. After some weeks, membranous light green heart-shaped 'shoots' grow from the spores followed later by young, slightly divided first leaves. Plant out in a shady place in soil well supplied with humus, ideally leaf mould. Water as required.

Collect the rhizome with about 2–3 cm ($\frac{3}{4}$–1 in) of the petioles. Clean and dry whole at a temperature of up to 35 °C (95 °F). The dried rhizome should remain green at the break. Store in well-sealed containers and protect from light.

The active constituents are extracted with ether and used to make medicines for treating parasitic worms, mainly tapeworms. It is poisonous in larger doses and should never, therefore, be used in home medicines and, in particular, should not be given to children.

Epilobium angustifolium L.
Rosebay Willowherb

Oenotheraceae

● Rosebay Willowherb is a perennial plant with stems up to 120 cm (47 in) in height. The creeping, richly branched rhizome has scaly protuberances. The stems are unbranched, erect, round and densely leafed. The leaves are alternate, either on short stalks or without stalks, tapering into a wedge shape towards the base, with a long point at the tip. They are slightly inrolled and imperceptibly toothed at the edges. The blade is a greyish green on the underside and has pronounced veins. The stem terminates in a rich raceme of flowers and buds growing from the axils of linear bracts. The calyx is formed of sepals fused at the base. They are red and downy on the outer side and the same length as the four petals, which are broadly oval and pinkish red. The flowers have a diameter of approximately 3 cm (1 in). There are eight stamens, the filaments of which widen at the base. From the inferior ovary grows a style curving upwards and terminating in a stigma which is club-shaped when young and later split into four parts. The ovary matures into long, densely downy capsules (1).

● Rosebay Willowherb grows in great abundance in clearings and open woodland, on shrubby slopes, sandbanks and screes, and to a lesser extent also on embankments and dumping grounds. It flourishes on lowlands and uplands. It flowers from May to August. The flowers open successively from the lower part of the inflorescence upwards: new buds are constantly growing at the tip, while, at the bottom of the stem, large numbers of seeds covered with white woolly down are released from the mature capsules.

Collect the leaves from flowering plants. The inflorescence and rhizomes may also be collected. Dry them in the shade.

European books on medicinal plants rather neglect Rosebay Willowherb, although it is highly valued in several parts of Asia. It has anti-inflammatory and tranquillizing properties. In France,

fresh leaves are placed on suppurating inflammations of the skin or on wounds. A decoction made from the inflorescence has diuretic and astringent properties and stimulates the dispersion of phlegm. In the USSR, a decoction made from the leaves is drunk instead of tea

for its tranquillizing and sleep-inducing effects. The Poles make an extract from the rhizomes to treat headaches. In other countries, a powder made from the leaves is sprinkled on wounds and the young tops of the fresh rhizomes are added to salads or cooked as a compote.

Equisetum arvense L.
Common Horsetail

VI–VIII

Equisetaceae

● This is a perennial, common weed growing to a height of 10−60 cm (4−24 in). Its branched, articulate rhizomes of a brownish-red colour sometimes penetrate down to 2 m (6 ½ ft) below ground. Their short lateral branches swell into globular propagating corms. In spring, the erect, yellowish to flesh-coloured, round, fragile and jointed fertile stems grow from the rhizome. The stem joints are bordered with light green sheaths which protrude in 9−12 tapering tips. The apex terminates in an oval cone of sporangia, which releases light green spores at maturity. The spring stalks soon die off and green summer stalks grow from other parts of the rhizome. They are sterile, furrowed, tough and articulate with the branches in whorls. They are bordered with cylindrical, brownish-green sheaths protruding in 9−12 tapering tips. The branches are similarly articulate with four-toothed sheaths and some with sparse further branching.

● Common Horsetail grows abundantly on sandy and loamy soils and is a common weed in fields, growing mainly in damp places. It is fertile from March to April.

Collect the sterile green summer stems, without the rhizomes. Cut them off at ground level and clean away any clinging soil and yellowing or brownish stalks. Collect in dry weather as they easily go mouldy. Dry them immediately after collection, spread out in thin layers at a temperature of up to 40 °C (104 °F). Carefully turn the stems during the drying process. The dried stems should remain green. Do not allow them to become damp, otherwise they will turn black and mouldy. Store in well-sealed glass containers or tins.

Diuretic teas made from Common Horsetail may help sufferers from kidney stones and other disorders of the urinary system. It has a haemostatic effect and may therefore be used for menstrual problems and bleeding haemorrhoids. It also has disinfectant properties. A decoction may be used to make compresses and to bathe skin complaints, slow-healing wounds, eczema, erysipelas, fungal diseases, varicose veins and abscesses on the legs. Gargling with a decoction may relieve tonsillitis and sore and bleeding gums and soothe the mouth after tooth extraction.

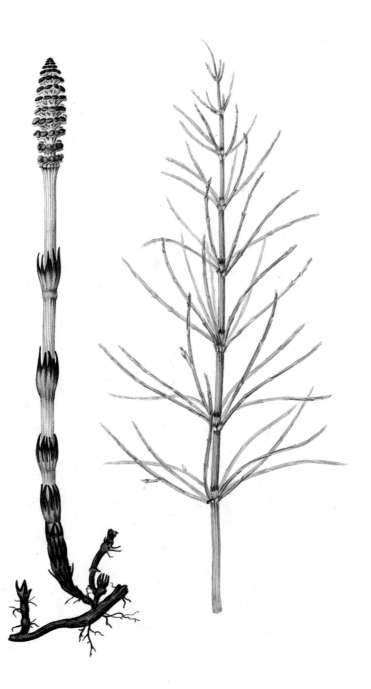

Diuretic and tonic tea: scald 20 ml (4 teaspoons) chopped dried stems with 400 ml (14 fl oz) boiling water. Take every other day.

74

Euonymus europaea L.
European Spindle-tree

Celastraceae

● This densely branched shrub or small tree grows to a height of 2—6 m (6 $\frac{1}{2}$—20 ft). The bark, even on older trunks, is smooth and greenish-grey. The shoots are green, square with rounded corners, the older twigs having four violet-brown, protruding bands. The ovate, pointed buds are opposite or arranged in opposite slanting pairs, appressed to the twigs, and covered with green, reddish-brown-bordered scales with fine hairs. The branches spread widely towards the sides. The leaves are opposite, oval or tapering, pointed, finely toothed and stalked. The blade is glabrous, rich green on the upper side and bluish on the underside. The bisexual, almost regular flowers (1) are arranged in sparse erect dichasia. The four small sepals are rounded. The four oval petals are fringed at the edges, broadly spreading and greenish white to yellowish. Among them are four stamens with kidney-shaped anthers. The superior ovary grows from a wide disc, maturing into a four-valved, pink to red capsule (2) containing the seeds (3).

● European Spindle-tree grows in lowland and upland forests, on rocky slopes, in valleys and on river banks. It flourishes on calcium-rich soil. It flowers from May to July.

For commercial processing, the bark from the branches or roots and the mature fruits are collected in autumn.

European Spindle-tree is a poisonous plant. The symptoms of poisoning are cold sweats, vomiting, diarrhoea and weakness. It should never be used for home medicines. The leaves and fruits have mild laxative properties and the fruits affect heart activity in the same way as the Foxglove. They were also once used to repel insects and for treating scabies. The bark stimulates the production of bile. The leaves and fruits lower blood pressure and this is a further reason for not using them in home medicines.

Euphrasia rostkoviana L.
Eyebright

Scrophulariaceae

● This is a small, annual parasitic plant. It has a branched root in the ground and lateral rootlets which cling to the roots of other plants. The erect, 10—30 cm (4—12 in) tall stem starts to branch at the bottom. It is almost round, richly leafed, softly hairy, articulate, and has stalked glands on the joints. The leaves are opposite, without stems, sometimes slightly enclosing, oval, sharply toothed and hairy, with dense, stalked glands at the edges.

The stalked, bisexual flowers grow in the axils of the bracts, which resemble the leaves. They are arranged in spikes at the tops of the branches. The tubular, glandular calyx has four pointed teeth. The corolla (1) is two-lipped and symmetrical. The corolla tube protrudes from the calyx when in full bloom, extending into a funnel shape at the top. It is white or pale violet with the upper lip coloured violet and a yellow spot on the lower lip. There are four stamens. The pistil is superior with a filament-like style and a club-shaped stigma. The fruit is an oval, two-valved and hairy capsule.

● Eyebright grows in damp meadows and pastures, in peat-bogs and in open woodland on lowlands and uplands. It flowers from July to September. Collect the whole haulm during the flowering period and dry in small bundles hung in the shade at a temperature of up to 40 °C (104 °F). Store in well-sealed containers.

In popular healing, a decoction is used to treat eye disorders, such as conjunctivitis and inflamed eyelids and to soothe tired or strained eyes. Taken internally, Eyebright stimulates the production of gastric juices, acts as a tonic and is used to treat nose and throat ailments. It also acts as an expectorant. The extract is taken for loss of appetite and digestive disorders, particularly biliousness and insufficient gastric juices. It is also popularly used for relieving spasms, severe headaches, hysteria, insomnia and fatigue.

> **Extract for loss of appetite and digestive disorders:** infuse 15 ml (1 tablespoon) dried haulm in 500 ml (18 fl oz) boiling water. Take in small sips during the day. Alternatively take 2—3 g ($\frac{1}{10}$ oz) powdered haulm daily.

V

 IX–X

XI–III

Fagus sylvatica L.
Beech

Fagaceae

● This 40 m (130 ft) tall tree has smooth silver-grey bark until old age. The shoots are slender and brown and the older twigs dark brown to brownish-grey, the lateral ones shortened and ringed. The buds are spindle-shaped, pointed and spreading from the twigs. The appressed, cinnamon-brown enclosing scales have a darker band in the centre. The leaves are alternate, entire or with blunt wavy teeth, and downy at the edges from spring to summer. The blade in mature leaves is glossy green and glabrous on the upper side and has small white hairs on the underside along the main nerve and in the angles of the lateral nerves. There are five to nine lateral nerves on each side. The leaf stalk is short. The flowers are heterosexual and the tree monoecious. The male flowers grow in globular, drooping catkins on long stalks. The individual tiny flowers have a yellowish perianth and 6–20 stamens. The female flowers grow in pairs in a small red, erect, scaly cupule. The fruits are three-sided achenes (1) in hard, prickly cups (2).

● Beech is distributed throughout western, central and southern Europe, extending to the north as far as southern Sweden and to the east as far as the southern Ukraine. It grows on lowlands and uplands on dry soil. At lower elevations, it usually grows in association with oak. At around 600 m (2,000 ft) above sea level, it often forms pure stands — beechwoods — and at higher altitudes grows together with fir, Mountain Maple and spruce. It is a very valuable woodland tree and is often cultivated in parks, particularly forms with variegated leaves or with drooping branches. It flowers at the same time as the leaves sprout in May. The fruits mature from the end of September, but mostly in October.

Beech is not important in popular medicine. Collect the young leaves and shoots with the sprouted foliage, the seeds and the bark. Dry them in the shade. In Spain, an extract made from the dried bark from young branches, gathered in early spring, is used to this day for treating intermittent fever. Larger doses of the drug have laxative effects and, if exceeded, cause vomiting. Charcoal made from beechwood was once used as medicinal charcoal for absorbing toxins in cases of poisoning. A tar-like liquid obtained by means of dry distillation of the wood can be applied to skin complaints and the oil pressed from the seeds is sometimes added to various ointments instead of petroleum jelly. A decoction made from the shoots and leaves may be added to baths for sufferers from rheumatism.

Filipendula ulmaria (L.) Maxim.
Meadowsweet

Rosaceae

● This is a perennial herb up to 150 cm (59 in) tall. An erect stem, which is branched at the apex, glabrous, tough and angular, grows from the articulate, creeping rhizome. The leaves are alternate, sparse and interruptedly odd-pinnate with broad heart-shaped stipules. They consist of one to five pairs of broadly ovate or tapering oval leaflets which are coarsely toothed and pointed. The blade is glabrous and dark green above and light green or white and felty below. The terminal leaflet is divided into three to five lobes. The stem bears a rich inflorescence of tiny yellowish-white flowers with five small, triangular to oval sepals, five free, oval petals and over 20 stamens with filaments longer than the corolla. At the centre of the flower there are five to ten pistils with a superior ovary, very short styles and club-shaped stigmas. From the oval ovaries develop spirally twisted glabrous follicles, each containing a single seed. When unripe they are green, later brown.

● Meadowsweet grows in damp meadows, ditches and bogs, at the edges of ponds, along the banks of streams and rivers and in damp open woodland on lowlands and uplands. It flowers from July to August.

The most effective medicinal substances come from the flowers. Pull them from the inflorescence on to a sheet of paper and dry as quickly as possible in the shade at a temperature of up to 40 °C (104 °F). In popular medicine, the whole inflorescence is also used and even the whole haulm and rhizome with the roots.

Meadowsweet is effective against fevers from chills, has diuretic properties, promotes sweating and is effective against bleeding and diarrhoea. A decoction from the inflorescence may be taken as an auxiliary medicine for rheumatism, influenza and other feverish illnesses. A decoction made from the leaves and flowers has fever-reducing and diuretic effects, bringing relief from kidney and bladder pain. Some skin rashes may be bathed with the decoction. The roots, which have the same curative properties, are taken as a powder three times a day in 3 g ($\frac{1}{10}$ oz) doses.

Fever-reducing and diuretic tea: scald 3 g ($\frac{1}{10}$ oz) dried haulm with 500 ml (18 fl oz) boiling water.

Extract for rheumatism, gout and complaints of the urinary system: macerate 5 ml (1 teaspoon) chopped dry haulm in 250 ml (9 fl oz) cold water for eight hours. Take during the day in sips.

Fragaria vesca L.
Wild Strawberry

Rosaceae

● Wild Strawberry is a perennial herb up to 20 cm (8 in) in height. It has a slanting branched rhizome. A basal rosette of leaves grows from it, and from the axils of these leaves grow creeping shoots with further rosettes of leaves which take root and produce new plants. The stems are erect, hairy, and sparsely branched at the top. The basal leaves on long petioles are three-lobed with tapering bracts. The petioles are hairy. The individual leaflets are oval, coarsely toothed and their teeth terminate in a red spine. The blade is hairy and dark green on the upper side, and has appressed shiny hair on the underside. From the main nerve six to nine small lateral veins run on each side. Single flowers grow from the axils of the three-lobed or simple leaflets with stipules. They have a small calyx of tapering sepals and triangular or oval petals. Both these are hairy and bend backwards as the fruit matures. The corolla is white, and the receptacle turns fleshy to form the familiar, red false fruit — the strawberry — with achenes (1) on the surface.

● Wild Strawberry grows on lowlands and uplands. It flowers from April to June, in some places repeatedly until September. The fruits mature in the second half of June and in July.

The basal leaves have medicinal properties. Pick them and dry in the shade. The leaves of cultivated varieties, which have arisen as crosses of several species, are not used. In popular healing, the fruits and rhizomes are also used.

A decoction made from Strawberry leaves may be drunk instead of tea. A decoction made from the young leaves (without the stalks) is a mild laxative and a diuretic. It is used to treat kidney complaints and, with the mature fruits, to treat gout. The famous botanist C. Linnaeus is said to have cured himself in this way. A decoction may be used on compresses for bleeding haemorrhoids and suppurating wounds and as a gargle to relieve sore gums. In Spain the fruits are recommended for anaemia. (However, diabetes, digestive disorders and obesity are contra-indications.) A strong decoction made from the leaves is recommended for diarrhoea, while a decoction made from the crushed, dried rhizome may be drunk as a diuretic tea and used as a gargle for sore throat and inflamed gums. Crushed leaves may be placed on abscesses and carbuncles, on freckles as an overnight treatment and on various skin problems. Allergy to the fruit is common, particularly in children, causing an irritating rash.

Tea: scald 3—5 g ($\frac{1}{10}$—$\frac{1}{5}$ oz) dried leaves with boiling water, leave to stand and strain.

79

Fraxinus excelsior L.
Ash

Oleaceae

● This tree grows up to 40 m (130 ft) tall and has a broadly oval crown. The width of the trunk may reach more than 1 m (39 in). The bark is smooth and grey until the tree is about 30 years old, and then it cracks slightly, usually verti- cally. The shoots are thick, erect, grey, cylindrical and flattened at the buds. The buds are opposite, oval, arranged in slanting pairs in the lower part of the twig, semi-globular, and covered with black scales. The opposite, erect, odd- pinnate leaves are formed of 9–13 tapering, pointed, coarsely-toothed leaflets, which are glabrous above and sparsely hairy below. The flowers ap- pear before the leaves, growing in erect, later drooping panicles. They are both bisexual and unisexual, being without flower envelopes. The bisexual flowers have two stamens with red anthers, a superior ovary with a short style and a two-lobed stigma. The male flowers have only stamens (1), the female ones a pistil and sterile deciduous stamens (2). The fruits develop into winged, flatly oval, brown achenes (3).

● The Ash is distributed throughout almost the whole of Europe, penetrat- ing far to the north and to the east. It grows mainly in river and stream valleys on both lowlands and uplands. It can also be found on screes and, in some places, on warmer rocky slopes. Varie- ties with undivided or white to yellow- spotted leaves are planted in parks. It flowers from April to May. The fruits mature in October and remain on the trees long into the winter.

Peel the bark from branches four to five years old or even older, from felled trees or from low branches cut off in spring before the leaves start to sprout. Dry it in the sun or by artificial heat and then grind it into powder. Collect the leaves in spring or at the beginning of summer in May and June, while they are still young. Dry them in the shade.

The leaves and bark have laxative properties. A decoction made from the leaves may be taken for kidney com- plaints, water retention, rheumatism and gout, and in order to increase the elimination of salts from the body.

The Polish pharmacopoeia recog- nizes the bark only as a diuretic and fever-reducing substance, recommend- ing it mainly for gout in the elderly and for kidney and bladder complaints. In France, Spain and Yugoslavia, the leaves are often processed into extracts, decoctions and syrups with diuretic and laxative effects. They are also recom- mended for treating fevers and are blended with other medicinal plants for treating rheumatism. An extract made from the leaves with boiling water may be used to bathe wounds.

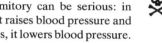

Fumaria officinalis L.
Common Fumitory

Papaveraceae

● Common Fumitory is an annual herb with a branched root. The erect stem is 10–30 cm (4–12 in) tall, branched, angular to furrowed, hollow and richly leafed. The leaves are stalked, alternate, double odd-pinnate and divided into fine-stalked, palmately or pinnately divided sections, which are linear, blunt or pointed, bluish-green and glabrous. The symmetrical bisexual flowers grow in erect, rich racemes (1), always positioned opposite the stem leaves. The calyx is formed of two toothed sepals which fall early. The corolla consists of four petals in two rows. The two outer ones are round at the front and purplish-red, the two inner ones wedge-shaped and elongated and fused at the tip. The corolla extends into a spur. There are two stamens. The superior ovary with one valve contains a single seed at the side. The style, with two stigmas, terminates in a blunt tubercle at the sides. The fruit is a kidney-shaped achene.

● Common Fumitory is a common weed in gardens and fields, on rubbish tips and waste land, in hedgerows and along walls and fences. It flowers from May to August. It is poisonous.

The whole haulm, without the roots, is collected during the flowering period and then dried in thin layers in the shade. The drying process can be completed in artificial heat. It is also dried hung in small bundles. The dried plant should retain its original colours.

Common Fumitory has a beneficial effect on the activity of the stomach, and there is evidence that it may be beneficial in the case of gallbladder disorders. Experiments on animals and in clinical practice have demonstrated that, under medical supervision, gallbladder patients have a good tolerance of this treatment, even for several months. It is effective against parasitic worms, is mildly laxative, has been used to treat sweating, digestive disorders, severe constipation, flatulence, gastric ulcers, haemorrhoids, persistent skin rashes and fatigue. The side-effects of taking Common Fumitory can be serious: in small doses, it raises blood pressure and in larger doses, it lowers blood pressure. Therefore, it should never be used in home medicines.

1

Galega officinalis L.
Goat's Rue

Leguminosae

● This perennial herb, up to 120 cm (47 in) tall, has a branched rhizome in the ground, from the tips of which grow numerous erect, tough, glabrous, longitudinally furrowed, mostly unbranched, hollow stems. The leaves are alternate, and borne on short stalks with tiny pointed stipules. They are odd-pinnate, composed of tapering oval leaflets terminating in a small pointed spine. Parallel, forked lateral veins run from their main nerve. Rich, long-stalked

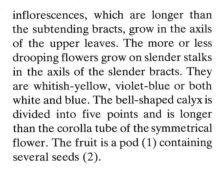

inflorescences, which are longer than the subtending bracts, grow in the axils of the upper leaves. The more or less drooping flowers grow on slender stalks in the axils of the slender bracts. They are whitish-yellow, violet-blue or both white and blue. The bell-shaped calyx is divided into five points and is longer than the corolla tube of the symmetrical flower. The fruit is a pod (1) containing several seeds (2).

● Goat's Rue is native to southern and eastern Europe. It is cultivated in some parts of central and western Europe as a fodder plant and as a medicinal plant. In many places, it has gone wild in river bank undergrowth, on damp meadows, in permanently inundated woods and in other warm damp places. It flowers in July and August.

Plant in damp, deep but airy, nutrient-rich soils. Sow the seeds in early spring directly in position, about 3—4 cm ($1-1\frac{1}{2}$ in) deep in rows 40—50 cm (16—20 in) apart. Prick out the seedlings to a distance of 40—50 cm (16—20 in) and apply fertilizer. They are harvested from the second or third year onwards, up to three times a year.

Collect the whole flowering haulm and dry in the shade at a temperature of up to 50 °C (122 °F). The leaves and flowers must retain their original colour. Store in well-sealed containers. Sometimes the seed is also collected.

Goat's Rue contains constituents which reduce the sugar level in the blood. It is sometimes used as an auxiliary medicine in the treatment of diabetes and in anti-diabetic teas. Diabetics should consult their doctors before taking any medicines. The haulm is recommended as a diuretic and fever-reducing medicine for treating feverish illnesses accompanied by a rash in children.

1

2

Galeopsis segetum NECK.
Downy Hemp-nettle

Labiatae

● An erect, 20–50 cm (8–20 in) tall, bluntly square, often reddish, hairy, richly branched stem grows from the simple, spindle-shaped root. The leaves are opposite, on long stalks, oval or tapering, coarsely toothed, entire in the wedge-shaped narrowed lower part, and, especially when young, covered with soft silky hair on both sides. The flowers grow in the axils of the highest pairs of leaves in groups of four to nine. They have a tubular, bell-shaped calyx with glossy, spreading hairs. It is divided approximately to a third of its length into lobes terminating in a small short spine. The corolla is symmetrical, sulphur yellow, and downy with a violet, purplish-pink or dark yellow spot on the lower lip. It is approximately three to four times as long as the calyx. Under the flowers, which have no stems, there are narrowly tapering, hairy bracts. Two long and two shorter stamens grow under the lower lip. The fruits are glabrous and oval.

● The plant is native to western Europe, where it grows as a weed on sandy soils in fields, on waste land and on non-calcareous rocks. It flowers in July and August.

It is cultivated for medicinal purposes. It does best in dry, sandy soils in which well-rotted manure was incorporated the autumn before sowing. Sow the seed in the spring in rows 35 cm (14 in) apart. Collect the whole haulm during the flowering period from July to August. Cut off the plants at ground level and dry in small bundles in the shade. The flowers should not lose their original colour.

Tea and syrups made from Downy Hemp-nettle are expectorant. It has astringent properties and is also recommended for kidney and bladder complaints. It is a mild laxative, stimulates the appetite and is a suitable tonic preparation for convalescence and anaemia. A decoction supplies minerals, especially trace elements. An extract may be used externally for compresses placed on slow-healing wounds and skin infections, particularly boils. For expectoration, the dried plant is often combined with others, especially Coltsfoot, Lungwort and Plantain, and, as a diuretic preparation, with Knotgrass and Horsetail.

Expectorant extract: macerate 15–25 g ($\frac{1}{2}$–$\frac{3}{4}$ oz) dried haulm in 400 ml (14 fl oz) water and take in doses of 100 ml (3 $\frac{1}{2}$ fl oz) three times a day.

Galium odoratum (L.) SCOP.

V–VI 🌿

(syn. *Asperula odorata* L.)

Woodruff

Rubiaceae

☠

● Woodruff is a low, perennial plant. The creeping, slender and branched rhizomes produce erect, smooth, 10–30 cm (4–12 in) tall, square stems. The stalks bear whorls of oval, dark green leaves with stipules. The leaves are glabrous, entire, rough at the margin and extended at the tips into a small, short spine. Some stalks are only leafed, others bear an inflorescence at the tip. The tiny white flowers have a funnel-shaped corolla divided into four lobes to which four stamens are attached. The pistil has a two-lobed stigma. The calyx is stunted. The fruits are double achenes composed of two globular or somewhat kidney-shaped parts (1). They bear prickly bristles which hook on to anything passing, such as clothes or the fur of animals. The whole plant has a spicy smell, especially when fading, and a bitter taste. It turns completely black when drying slowly.

● Woodruff is widespread in woods, particularly beechwoods, and forms large patches. In places, it has even remained in coniferous woods. It flowers in May and June.

Collect both the flowering and non-flowering haulm, either during flowering or shortly before. Cut off the plant just above the ground. Do not pull it off, otherwise parts of the rhizomes will also come away. Dry in the shade and do not allow it to become damp afterwards. Store in well-sealed containers. Other dried plants readily absorb its smell.

The fresh haulm is used externally for compresses or taken internally as an extract with stimulant properties, whereas the extract made from the dried haulm has a tranquillizing effect. It relieves several painful complaints without actually curing them. Long-term use can seriously damage your health and even cause severe poisoning. Therefore, Woodruff should never be used in home medicines. Small doses cause dizziness, headache and vomiting, larger doses paralysis and even death. It also reduces the ability of the blood to coagulate.

1

Galium verum L.
Lady's Bedstraw

Rubiaceae

● This perennial herb is 20–100 cm (8–39 in) tall. It has a creeping rhizome composed of short joints. This produces shrubby clumps of erect, glabrous or downy, round, articulate stems with four low, narrow ridges. The leaves, in whorls of 6–12, are linear, pointed, inrolled at the edges, dark green and glabrous or downy above and white-felted with a prominent white main nerve below. At their ends, the stems bear dense rich panicles of tiny flowers with felty stalks which grow from the axils of the linear bracts. The calyx is completely stunted into an inconspicuous green border. The corolla is a rich yellow to golden yellow, and divided into four blunt lobes (1). Four stamens with brown anthers grow alternately among these. The flowers are honey-scented. The fruits are glabrous, smooth, brownish achenes.

● Lady's Bedstraw is widespread in pastures, meadows, open woodland and other grassy places. It flowers from July to August and, on mown meadows, for a second time in August and September.

Collect the whole haulm during the flowering period. Cut it off at ground level, tie in small bundles and hang to dry in the shade.

A decoction made from the dried haulm may be taken for gastric upsets and biliousness. It has anti-bacterial, haemostatic and anti-spasmodic properties. It is recommended as a diuretic preparation for disorders of the urinary system and for dropsy. In popular medicine it is also used to promote sweating and reduce fever. The fresh haulm, an extract made from the dried haulm or alcohol extracts may be used to treat various skin complaints, such as slow-healing wounds, rashes and boils, either in the form of compresses or by bathing the affected area directly. Fungal infections, impetigo and weeping scabs may be treated with a decoction made from Chamomile and Horsetail, and then with compresses made from a decoction of Soapwort rhizomes, Birch leaves and the haulm of Lady's Bedstraw.

1

Extract to relieve inflammation of the lower urinary tract: macerate 15–30 ml (1–2 tablespoons) chopped dried haulm in 1 litre (1 $\frac{3}{4}$ pints) boiling water for about 15 minutes. Strain.

Geranium robertianum L.
Herb Robert

Geraniaceae

● This annual, sometimes biennial, herb has a branched taproot with an abundance of fine rootlets. A rosette of basal leaves grows from the root. The first of these leaves are deeply palmately indented into three further divided sections, and the following ones are palmately divided into up to five parts with the sections further pinnately indented. The sections terminate in small spines. Their stalks, main nerves and edges are usually carmine red. The stems are erect or grow along the ground and are 20–40 cm (8–16 in) long. The basal leaves wither when the stems have grown. The stem is oval, with fine spreading hair, often reddish to carmine-red at the base, and forked. The stem leaves are opposite, stalked, mostly deeply palmately indented into three sections, and further pinnately indented. The flowers grow in pairs on long stalks from the leaf axils. The calyx is divided into five lobes. The corolla (1) is composed of ovate, carmine-pink, rarely white, petals and 10 stamens. The superior ovary has five styles, fused to form a beak shape. The fruit later splits into five parts.

● Herb Robert grows in woods and clearings, in hedgerows, on shaded rocks and walls, and on damp rocky screes on lowlands and uplands. It flowers from May to October.

Collect the flowering haulm, and dry it in natural heat in the shade, or by artificial heat up to a temperature of 40 °C (104 °F).

In popular medicine, an extract or decoction is taken internally for diarrhoea, haemorrhaging, diseases of the urinary system, kidney stones, jaundice and gallbladder disorders because the herb has astringent, anti-diarrhoea and diuretic properties. A decoction is used externally for treating conjunctivitis and wounds, and on compresses to relieve pain, on inflammatory skin conditions, erysipelas, persistent rashes (especially when other methods of cure have not been effective) and contusions. Most popular healing techniques have not been scientifically verified but it seems that Herb Robert and related species have haemostatic, diuretic, and to some extent also antiseptic effects. Gargling with an extract of the dried haulm may help sore throats and it can be used as a mouth wash to treat bleeding and infected gums.

1

Diuretic tea: infuse 5 ml (1 teaspoon) chopped dried haulm in 200 ml (7 fl oz) boiling water.

Geum urbanum L.
Herb Bennet

Rosaceae

● Herb Bennet is a perennial weed up to 75 cm (30 in) tall. It has a slanting, unbranched rhizome and a small tuft of strong, small brown roots from which the basal rosette of leaves grows. These are stalked, interruptedly odd-pinnate and with a large, heart-shaped terminating section, divided by deep incisions into three to five lobes. There are several erect, sparsely branched, angular, downy stems. The stem leaves are alternate, the lower ones in three parts, the upper ones three-lobed with large stipules. The blade is covered on both sides with spreading hairs and stalked glands. The flowers (1) grow singly from the leaf axils on long, erect stalks, which are downy and covered with glandular hairs. They have an epicalyx consisting of narrow linear sections and a calyx composed of tapering oval, hairy points, which later bend backwards away from the fruit. The petals are oval and bright yellow. There are numerous stamens and pistils. The achenes (2), which terminate in a small hook, grow in a cluster.

● Herb Bennet is common in gardens, hedges, ditches, open woodland, on dumping grounds, untended meadows and other waste places. It flourishes on lowlands and uplands. It flowers from May to October.

Collect the rhizome with the roots in April and May. Sometimes the whole haulm is also collected. Wash the roots thoroughly and dry slowly in moderate heat. The dried root is dark brown and crumbly.

Herb Bennet was formerly used as a spice, as a substitute for cloves. For medicinal purposes, it is mainly used to treat digestive disorders. To improve the appetite, prepare an extract by macerating 50 g (1 $\frac{3}{4}$ oz) dried rhizome in 500 ml (18 fl oz) wine for eight days, and take 5 ml (1 teaspoon) before meals. Herb Bennet may be taken for chronic bronchitis. A decoction may be used as a gargle or mouth rinse for treating bleeding and inflamed gums and bad breath. It is also said to have beneficial tranquillizing effects on the nervous system.

1

2

Alcohol extract for digestive disorders: boil 10 g ($\frac{2}{5}$ oz) dried rhizome for five minutes in 80 ml (3 fl oz) water. Add 80 ml (3 fl oz) pure spirit and macerate for eight days. Strain and take 15 ml (1 tablespoon) three times a day before each meal.

Glechoma hederacea L.
Ground Ivy

Labiatae

● This perennial, pleasantly scented, creeping herb is 10—20 cm (4—8 in) tall. The rooting, ascending branches are up to 80 cm (31 in) long. The stem is sporadically covered with spreading hair, rarely almost glabrous, and branched. Besides the erect flowering branches, non-flowering, creeping runners also grow from the stem joints. The leaves are opposite and stalked. The lower ones are kidney-shaped and broader than long, the upper ones are broadly heart-shaped or round, with a heart-shaped indentation at the stalk and a roughly toothed margin. The stalked flowers grow in groups of two to three in the leaf axils in the central and upper parts of the ascending branches. They have a tubular, symmetrical calyx with spreading hairs, divided into three larger and two smaller teeth, with 15 prominent small veins. The blue-violet, symmetrical, two-lipped corolla narrows in a funnel shape into a lighter, almost white trumpet, which has a crown of hairs at the mouth (1). The upper lip is indented into two lobes, the lower one being larger and three-lobed with darker violet spots (2). The fruits are smooth, square nutlets.

● Ground Ivy grows in gardens, on damp lawns, in hedges beside streams, in woods, shady meadows and damp fields. It is common on both lowlands and uplands. It flowers mainly in April and May, and sometimes repeatedly, even in autumn.

Collect the flowering branches in the spring months. Dry them in the shade so that they do not lose their colour. They may be eaten fresh as a vegetable in soups, stuffings and so on.

Ground Ivy is a great favourite in popular healing and is widely used as a preparation for stimulating the appetite and digestion, and for improving the metabolism. It is effective chiefly as an astringent, an astrictive medicine and against diarrhoea. It is also useful in treating lung complaints and asthma because it encourages expectoration, as well as inflammation of the lower urinary tract. It is said to have beneficial effects on bile production and is, therefore, used to treat gastric and duodenal ulcers, gallstones and gallbladder diseases. Compresses prepared from Ground Ivy may be applied to skin ailments, especially inflammation, and to pimples. Ground Ivy is rarely used on its own; usually it is blended with other dried herbs to make a tea suitable for treating the health problems described above. It is given in the form of a hot decoction. In rare cases, the fresh juice is also used.

1

2

Extract from the Polish pharmacopoeia for a tonic: infuse 5—7.5 ml (1—1 $\frac{1}{2}$ teaspoons) dried herb in 400 ml (14 fl oz) hot water. Take 100 ml (3 $\frac{1}{2}$ fl oz) two to three times a day.

Extract for external use for compresses and bathing: infuse 15—25 g ($\frac{1}{2}$—$\frac{3}{4}$ oz) in 400 ml (14 fl oz) hot water for three minutes.

Glycyrrhiza glabra L.
Liquorice

Fabaceae

● Liquorice is a perennial herb up to 150 cm (59 in) tall. It has a long underground rhizome with numerous lateral runners which are strikingly yellow when cut (1). The upper part is usually swollen into a club shape and from it grow erect, branched stems which are rough at the top. The leaves are alternate, on short stalks, odd-pinnate, with small deciduous bracts. They have four to eight pairs of oval leaflets, which are entire, blunt at the tip, narrowed into a wedge shape towards the main axis, glabrous above and finely glandular on the underside. The petiole and axis of the leaf have a grooved depression and are covered with tiny hairs. Clusters of slender flowers, which are shorter than the supporting leaves, grow in the axils of some of the stem leaves. The flowers grow on stalks from the axils of tiny bracts. The calyx is a short bell shape and is glandular-hairy and divided into five tapering points. The corolla is symmetrical, light blue-violet, and yellowish-white on the wing sides. The fruits are leathery, reticulate, reddish-brown pods, which spread from the stem and contain three to five seeds.

● This herb, native to the Mediterranean and Asia Minor, flowers in June and July. The rhizomes have medicinal properties. They are obtained from cultivated plants and harvested at the end of summer and in autumn. They are dried by artificial heat at a temperature of up to 35 °C (95 °F).

The plant requires deep soil, rich in nutrients, and a dry, sunny location. Before sowing the seed or planting rhizome cuttings, prepare by digging, raking and incorporating fertilizer. Sow the seeds in March to April; they germinate within four to five weeks. Propagation from cuttings is better. Take 10 cm (4 in) long cuttings with at least two buds from the lateral branches

of the rhizome. Plant 60 cm (24 in) apart in April, or after harvesting the mature rhizomes in September and October. The first rhizomes may be harvested after three to four years and, with adequate care, the plants may survive for up to 20 years.

Decoctions may be taken for coughs, respiratory ailments, kidney stones and gout. Liquorice is also a well-known laxative. Extracts are used in the case of gastric ulcers to reduce tension and irritability in the stomach. Liquorice should not be used for a long time without medical supervision. Its side-effects include swelling of the face, later of the legs and hands, migraine, raised blood pressure and increased excretion of water and salts from the body.

1

> **Expectorant extract:** macerate 30 ml (2 tablespoons) finely cut rhizome in water for 10 minutes. Take 15 ml (1 tablespoon) five times a day.

Hedera helix L.
Ivy

Araliaceae

III—IV, VIII

VIII—X flowering shoots

This creeping or climbing woody plant grows to a length of up to 20 m (66 ft). The richly branched stem either creeps along the ground or climbs up supports, clinging to them with adhesive rootlets on the underside. The leaves are simple, evergreen, opposite, bractless, hairy when young and later glabrous, with tough, leathery, dark green and glossy blades, which are lighter and prominently veined underneath. They are of two types: the non-flowering stalks bear three- of five-lobed leaves; the fertile flowering branches oval to broadly tapering, long-pointed ones. Both types are stalked and entire. The flowers grow on old branches in the sun in semi-globular umbels in the axils of scale-like bracts (1). They are regular and hermaphrodite with an inconspicuous five-toothed calyx and a corolla of five fleshy petals which are brown on the outside and green inside. The five stamens bear oval anthers. The semi-inferior ovary with its short style matures into black berries with three to five kidney-shaped seeds.

Ivy grows in rocky woodland, on rocks, in hedges, and on old trees and walls. It is common in cemeteries, parks and gardens, from where it also often escapes. It flowers from August to October, sometimes even up to winter, the fruits only maturing the following year in spring. The hairs on the young shoots can cause skin irritation in sensitive people.

The leaves and flowering shoots have medicinal properties, but all parts of the plant are poisonous. The leaves are collected in March and April and in August and dried in the sun. The flowering shoots are collected from the tops of mature Ivy and are used, mainly fresh, externally.

All parts of the plant contain substances that affect the activity of the heart and the vascular system. Moderate doses widen the vessels, but larger doses narrow them and slow down the activity of the heart. Ivy also stimulates liver and gallbladder activity. As Ivy is poisonous and has powerful effects on the circulation and on heart activity, it should never be used in home medicines. The fresh leaves or flowering shoots, either crushed, or, if sterility is essential, scalded with boiling water, may be placed on slow-healing and inflamed wounds. In cosmetics, the fresh juice from the leaves is used for softening hard skin on the feet, corns, calluses and so on.

90

Hepatica nobilis GARS.
Hepatica

Ranunculaceae

● This low perennial herb is one of the first messengers of spring. It has a spindle-shaped, rather woody rhizome. In spring simple, leafless, hairy stems grow, each bearing a single violet, pink or, rarely, white flower. There is an irregular number, usually 6–12, of the petal-like, coloured perianth segments. Under these there are three small, oval, entire, sessile stem leaves arranged in a whorl, so that they look like the calyx. The flowers bear a large number of stamens with yellow anthers, and many pistils with ovaries clustered into small globular heads. When the flowers have faded, basal leaves on long, hairy petioles grow from the rhizome. They are usually three-lobed (1), exceptionally up to five-lobed (2). The blades are glossy, green, often with paler spots above, and softly hairy below. The leaflets are heart-shaped. The leaves last a long time past the winter, withering only in spring before the new flowers grow. The fruits are green achenes, yellowish at the base, terminating in short beak-shapes.

● Hepatica is a widespread European plant growing in shady, mainly deciduous forests and hedges and on rocky slopes. It occurs mainly on lowlands. It flowers in March and April, in May and June on uplands.

The leaves have medicinal properties but are not used in home medicines. Hepatica was once a favourite medicine in popular healing, particularly for treating diseases of the liver and gallbladder. This was probably because the shape of the leaves and the leaf spots are reminiscent of a diseased liver. The tannin in the leaves has an astringent effect on haemorrhaging, and the plant was also used to treat kidney and bladder diseases, particularly when blood appeared in the urine. It has also been used in cases of bringing up blood from the lungs. As Hepatica contains substances which act as a heart poison it should never be used in home medicines. Moreover, the diseases mentioned are so serious that immediate medical advice is essential.

1

2

91

Herniaria glabra L.
Smooth Rupturewort

Silenaceae

This is a small, annual to perennial herb. Prostrate stems grow in all directions from the taproot. They are 5–15 cm (2–6 in) long, richly branched, yellowish-green, glabrous or downy. These form flat, round cushions up to 30 cm (12 in) in diameter. The stems are densely covered with numerous opposite, almost sessile leaves and small, white, dry membranous stipules. The leaf blade is oval, quite thick and either with spreading hairs at the edges or glabrous. One of the pair of leaves at the end of the stem usually does not develop, so that the leaves appear to be alternate. In the leaf axils, small flowers cluster in globular dichasia, which are spike-like at the ends of the stems. The flower (1) has five oval, yellowish-green sepals, five whitish petals shorter than the calyx, five stamens and a pistil with a long style. The semi-inferior ovary matures into a globular nutlet which falls with the calyx and remains closed. Each contains a single black seed.

Smooth Rupturewort grows on acid or neutral soils, in dry, sandy or stony places, in fields and on ridges. It flowers from June to September.

Cut off the haulm with scissors at ground level, as it is considerably polluted when the whole plant is pulled up. The most suitable period for collection is July and August when the plants are already well developed but not yet withering. Dry them as quickly as possible in the shade, spread out in thin layers at a temperature of up to 40 °C (104 °F). Plants from warm, sunny positions have more active constituents than plants growing in the shade. When stored for longer periods, or if dried incorrectly, the active substances decompose very quickly, so store in well-sealed containers.

The plants can also be cultivated in dry, sandy soils. Sow the seed in March in rows 25 cm (10 in) apart. Depending on the temperature, it will germinate within three to four weeks. The beds only need weeding.

Smooth Rupturewort has disinfectant properties and relieves spasms of the upper and lower urinary tract. It forms part of diuretic teas with other similarly acting drugs (for example Bearberry and Cranberry leaves) and an extract may be taken to relieve inflammation of the bladder, kidney stones and other kidney ailments, and to treat prostate trouble in the elderly. However, Smooth Rupturewort should only be used by trained doctors and not in home medicines.

1

Hippophae rhamnoides L.
Sea Buckthorn

Eleagnaceae

● Sea Buckthorn is a thorny shrub or tree up to 10 m (33 ft) in height. The annual shoots are erect, golden-brown and glossy, the older twigs a dark brown. The blackish-brown outer bark on the thick branches and trunk peels off in scales. The terminal and lateral twigs usually end in a thorn. The alternate, angularly globular buds are covered in rusty brown, shiny scales. The leaves are alternate, narrowly tapering and entire. On the upper side they are greyish-green and on the underside silvery white and felty with slightly inrolled edges. It is dioecious and the very small flowers are unisexual. The male flowers are clustered underneath the annual shoots, and the female ones (1) are arranged in racemes. The flowers lack both a calyx and a corolla. The male ones (2) have only two rusty yellow perianth segments, four stamens with very short filaments and yellow anthers; the female ones only a tubular perianth with a superior ovary and a long style. The fruits are orange, barrel-shaped drupes.

● Sea Buckthorn is native to southern, western and northern Europe, where it grows on sand dunes along the coast and on the gravelly deposits of rivers. It is sometimes cultivated both as an ornamental tree and also for its fruits. It flowers before the leaves in April and May.

Propagate from root cuttings taken from female plants. A small number of cuttings from male plants should also be planted for pollination. Plant the cuttings in a glasshouse or frame. When propagating from seed, it is necessary to remove the pulp from the pips, as this slows down germination. Break them up carefully and wash the seeds in water. Plant out the seedlings in the second or third year.

Collect the fruits as they are beginning to ripen, when they are starting to turn orange but are not yet soft. They are processed fresh by the pharmaceutical industry into vitamin preparations, and at home into jams and juices. To avoid damaging the vitamin C content, do not allow the fruits or the products made from them to come into contact with metal and do not cook at high temperatures for a long time.

The fruits are a rich source of vitamins C and A, and may be used as a tonic in cases of vitamin deficiency, general debility, reduced resistance during infectious illness and during convalescence. In popular healing in Poland, the leaves and bark are also used. They are rich in tannins and are taken internally to treat digestive disorders, mainly diarrhoea and haemorrhaging, and used externally for some skin inflammations.

93

Humulus lupulus L.
Hop

Canabaceae

● This perennial, climbing herb grows up to 6 m (20 ft) tall. The rhizome is creeping and richly branched, and numerous roots grow from it. Young shoots which appear in spring are coiled in a spiral at first, and later develop into clockwise-twining, tough, six-sided stems covered with tough, hooked hairs.

The leaves are opposite, on long petioles, and the blades of very diverse shapes, either undivided, heart-shaped or three- to five-lobed. They are very roughly toothed on the edges and, particularly on the underside, very rough with yellow glands. Two membranous bracts grow at the base of each leaf stalk. The flowers are unisexual, the plants dioecious. The male flowers grow in axillary or terminal panicles (1) and have five light yellow or greenish star-like perianth segments and five stamens. The inconspicuous female flowers (2) are in short spikes in the leaf axils. From the spikes later develop the drooping, glandular, light green, pale yellow to reddish hop-cones (3).

● Hops grow along river banks, in scrub and damp woodland. Widely cultivated, many plants have gone wild, developing from broken-off pieces of rhizome in ditches and hedges. The plant flowers from May to July, and is fertile from the end of August to September. Only the female plants are cultivated in hop fields, as pollination is not required. Therefore, male plants growing near hop fields are destroyed.

Only the female cones have medicinal properties. The most valuable are the sterile cones from cultivated plants. The active constituents are found mainly in glands, which break off and fall to form a yellow powder — lupulin. Collect the cones when they are fully developed at the end of August and the beginning of September. Dry them carefully at a temperature of 40–50 °C (104–122 °F). Store in the dark in well-sealed containers. They lose their efficacy with long storage. Hops are mainly used by the brewing industry.

Dried Hop forms part of tranquillizing preparations for treating nervous irritability and insomnia. It stimulates the digestion and the appetite and reduces sexual desire. It acts as a natural antibiotic. In popular healing, it is also used as a diuretic, for bladder inflammation, jaundice and other liver complaints. It is also believed to have beneficial effects on blood pressure.

> **Alcohol extract for insomnia:** macerate 20 g ($\frac{3}{4}$ oz) dried Hop in 100 ml ($3\frac{1}{2}$ fl oz) spirit for three days. Take 20 drops on a sugar cube before retiring.

Hyoscyamus niger L.
Henbane

Solanaceae

● This is a biennial, rarely an annual, herb. It has a spindle-shaped, beet-like enlarged root. A rosette of basal leaves grows first and later, usually only in the second year, an erect, simple or only slightly branched stem grows. This is up to 80 cm (31 in) tall, bluntly angled and covered with sticky hairs. The leaves are alternate, simple, oval, deeply toothed and lobed-pinnate to indented. Their sections are pointed. The lower leaves are stalked, the upper ones semi-enclosing. The blade is a matt greyish-green in colour on both sides, especially along the nerves and at the edges, and like the petiole, is covered with sticky hairs. The midrib is broad and lighter in colour. The sessile flowers, arranged in single elongating monochasia, grow from the axils of the upper leaves. They have a bell-shaped, glandularly hairy, markedly veined calyx running into five sharply pointed tips and a funnel-shaped, dirty yellow, externally hairy corolla with violet veins and a reddish-violet mouth. The fruits are capsules containing up to 500 greyish-brown seeds.

● Henbane grows on dumping grounds, on disturbed land and sometimes even as a weed in gardens and fields. It grows mainly on lowlands. Overwintering plants flower in May and June, the annual ones in July and August. In some countries, it is cultivated for pharmaceutical purposes. All parts of the plant are extremely poisonous.

The leaves, the whole haulm and the seeds are used by the pharmaceutical industry. The leaves and haulms are dried as quickly as possible to retain their original colour. The seed is collected shortly before maturing. The cut fertile tops of the plants are left to mature in a dry place and then threshed and the seed is laid out to dry out completely. Henbane is a powerful narcotic and a deadly poison. It should never be handled, except by professionals, and never used in home medicines.

It is processed only in the pharmaceutical industry into medicines for treating asthma, spasms and pain. Anti-asthmatic cigarettes are also manufactured from the leaves.

Hypericum perforatum L.
Perforate St John's Wort

Hypericaceae

● Perforate St John's Wort is a perennial herb. It has a richly branched rhizome, which often spreads out over a large surface. Both densely leafy, sterile stems and flower-bearing stems grow from the rhizome. The stems are erect, 30–60 cm (12–24 in) tall, branched at the top and rather tough, with two slightly protruding ridges. The leaves are opposite and sessile or on very short stalks, oval to linear, glabrous and entire. Against the light the thicker veins show through, as well as the dot-like small glands which contain an essential oil. The flowers are arranged in rich panicles, and have 5 pointed, tapering to oval sepals and five petals which are asymmetrical, toothed along one side, oval and golden yellow, with black dot-like glands at the edges. There are 50–60 stamens which are fused in the lower part into three bundles. There are three styles on a superior ovary. The fruit is a capsule which opens by three valves.

● This plant grows on sunny, shrubby slopes, in dry meadows, pastures and open woodland, on rocks, screes, waste land, in trenches and in clearings. It flourishes on lowlands and uplands, especially on calcareous soil.

Collect the flowering haulm or the flowers only. Cut off the upper parts of the plants to a length of 20–30 cm (8–12 in) and dry them hung up in small bundles in the shade. If they are dried in artificial heat, the temperature must not exceed 35 °C (95 °F). The dried plant should retain its original colour. Perforate St John's Wort contains constituents which have beneficial effects on the metabolism and bile excretion, improve circulation, reduce the urge to cough, and have a tranquillizing effect on the nervous system. An extract made with boiling water is taken for disorders of the digestive and excretory systems, kidney diseases and restless sleep. An oil is used to treat burns, sunburnt skin, wounds and haemorrhoids. The oil is prepared by macerating the chopped flowering haulm in vegetable oil. This is exposed to the sun for about a fortnight and shaken several times during this period. This treatment causes photosensitivity, so that if treated skin is exposed to the sun, skin inflammations can occur.

Alcohol extract for loss of appetite: macerate 25 g ($\frac{4}{5}$ oz) dried haulm in 125 ml (4 $\frac{1}{2}$ fl oz) spirit for three days. Take 2.5 ml ($\frac{1}{2}$ teaspoon) in a glass of water before meals.

Extract with tranquillizing properties: infuse 15 ml (1 tablespoon) chopped dried haulm in 500 ml (18 fl oz) boiling water.

Hyssopus officinalis L.
Hyssop

Labiatae

● Hyssop is a perennial, richly branched sub-shrub. It has a woody rhizome. Tufts of ascending 20—50 cm (8—20 in) tall, richly branched and densely leafy stems grow from it. The stems are square and covered with downy hair. The leaves are opposite, almost sessile, narrowly tapering, blunt-tipped, leathery, glossy, almost glabrous with sessile small glands, and are entire with inrolled edges. The flowers grow in groups of three to seven in the axils of the upper leaves, forming single terminal spikes. The awl-shaped bracts under the flowers are shorter than the leaf-stalks. The symmetrical flowers have a tubular calyx which is red or violet in colour, downy and divided up to a quarter or even a half of its height into five teeth, which are tapering and terminate in a small spine. The two-lipped corolla (1) is violet, more rarely pink or yellow-white, with the tube about as long as the calyx. The pistil has a violet style and a bifurcate stigma which protrudes from the corolla. The fruits are brown nutlets.

● Hyssop is native to the Mediterranean. It is cultivated as a spice and as a medicinal or melliferous plant. It sometimes temporarily turns wild. It flowers from July to October.

Collect the haulm from cultivated plants in July and August and dry, spread out in thin layers, in the shade. If it is dried by artificial heat, the temperature must not exceed 35 °C (95 °F). Store in well-sealed containers.

The plant can be propagated both from seed and vegetatively. Sow the seed in frames in early spring. Prick out the seedlings in May, 40 cm (16 in) apart in rows 50 cm (20 in) apart. It requires light sandy-loamy soils with a sufficient calcium content and a sunny and sheltered location. The soil must not be acid. Hyssop can also be propagated by dividing the clumps. The upper parts of the plants are cut off only once in the first year; twice in a season in subsequent years.

Hyssop has fever-reducing properties similar to those of Sage and also stimulates digestion and facilitates expectoration. An extract may be taken internally to treat chronic bronchitis, gastric ulcers and inflammation of the intestinal tract, mainly in the elderly. It has antibacterial properties and may be used externally for compresses on inflammatory skin complaints and as a mouth rinse. Hyssop must be used with care, as excessive doses affect the brain centres and can cause nervous disorders, accompanied by trembling. Hyssop is an aromatic plant and is used in the manufacture of liqueurs and cosmetics.

Inula helenium L.
Elecampane

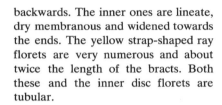

Compositae

● Elecampane is a handsome perennial herb, about 1.5 m (5 ft) tall, with a thick, cylindrical, branched, not very long rhizome. An erect, sparsely branched, tough, furrowed stem, with spreading hair in the lower part and felty above, grows from it. The basal leaves are oval, narrowing gradually in a wedge shape into the winged petiole, pointed at the tip and blunt-toothed at the edges. The stem leaves are alternate, irregularly toothed at the margin, large, a tapering oval or heart-shaped oval in shape, with a heart-shaped base, sessile to short-tapered. The blade has sparse short hair on the upper side and silky grey felt on the underside. The flower heads grow singly at the ends of the branches from the axils of the leaves or bracts. Sometimes they are even arranged in sparse umbels. The outer, inwardly-turned bracts are oval and felty on the outside with a large, heart-shaped, green appendix which bends backwards. The inner ones are lineate, dry membranous and widened towards the ends. The yellow strap-shaped ray florets are very numerous and about twice the length of the bracts. Both these and the inner disc florets are tubular.

● Elecampane originates from central Asia. In Europe, it is cultivated as an ornamental and medicinal plant and, in some places, has grown wild in hedgerows or on wet meadows. It flowers from June to October.

It is grown either from seed or cuttings taken from the upper part of the rhizomes. Sow the seed in March in frames. It germinates in the light at a temperature of 20−30 °C (68−86 °F) within 10−28 days. Plant out in the autumn 50 cm (20 in) apart in rows 35 cm (14 in) apart. Hoe and weed the beds up to five times during the year. It does best in damp, loamy soils.

Harvest the rhizomes with roots from the two- or three-year-old plants in the autumn. To ensure the rhizomes develop well, cut off the flowering tops during the summer. Cut off the whole plant before digging up the rhizome. Rinse with water and cut them in half or quarters lengthwise. Dry them as quickly as possible in thin layers by artificial heat at a temperature of up to 35 °C (95 °F). They quickly become damp and so should be stored in well-sealed containers.

An extract is taken internally to improve expectoration and stimulate bile production. It has beneficial effects on gastric activity and stimulates the digestion and appetite. It is also used against intestinal parasites and checks the reproduction of bacteria and microscopic pathogenic fungi.

Expectorant extract: infuse 25 g ($\frac{4}{5}$ oz) dried rhizome in 150 ml (5 fl oz) water and take in doses of 5−10 ml (1−2 teaspoons) several times daily.

For stimulating the appetite and to treat flatulence: take 100 ml ($3\frac{1}{2}$ fl oz) in three doses daily.

Iris germanica L.
Garden Iris

Iridaceae

● Garden Iris is a perennial herb. The thick, creeping rhizome is composed of flat joints thickened into a barrel shape and growing on the surface of the soil. An abundance of cylindrical small, light brown roots grow on the underside of the rhizome. An erect, 50—100 cm (20—39 in) tall, leafy stem, which is branched at the top, grows from the top of the rhizome. The leaves are sword-shaped, pointed and have a greyish tinge. The top of the rhizome from which the flower-bearing stem has grown does not grow further and is replaced by lateral branches. The stem leaves are alternate. In the upper part they are replaced by shorter bracts with boat-shaped depressions which are membranous in the upper half. The large, blue-violet flowers grow on very short stalks from the membranous bracts. These are regular and fused at the base in the trumpet. The three outer petals are bent and the three inner ones erect and hairy with fine veins. The anthers of the three stamens are situated under the stigma lobes. The inferior ovary is enclosed in bracts. The style is divided into three leaf-like lobes.

● Garden Iris is native to the Mediterranean and is widely cultivated in gardens as an ornamental. It flowers in May and June. The flowers fade quickly and after pollination develop into three-celled capsules with many flat, brown seeds.

Propagate either by division of the lateral rhizome joints or from the offset buds which form in large quantities at the sides of the rhizomes. Do this in August and September or March and April. Divide the rhizomes into parts with at least one offset bud each and plant in shallow furrows 10 cm (4 in) deep and 30 cm (12 in) apart. It requires a light, well-drained, loamy soil, rich in calcium. It does best in a sunny location. Weed and loosen the soil as necessary.

Collect the rhizomes in the third and fourth years, ideally after rain, in August or at the beginning of September, when they are juicy. Remove the leaves, stalks and thin roots and wash, peel, rinse and dry the rhizomes in thin layers on racks at a temperature of up to 35 °C (95 °F). The dried rhizome should remain yellowish-white in colour. Store in well-sealed containers.

Garden Iris facilitates expectoration and has disinfectant properties. It forms part of medicinal anti-tussive teas and is used for treating bronchial catarrh and gallbladder complaints. Powdered rhizome may be sprinkled on some skin ailments. Oil pressed from it is used by the cosmetic, perfume, liqueur and food industries.

Juniperus communis L.
Juniper

Cupressaceae

● Juniper is an evergreen coniferous shrub or richly branched small tree up to 10 m (33 ft) in height. It is a dioecious plant. The slender male plants have a spindle-shaped crown, the female ones being rather broadly spreading, and often of shrubby growth with a broadly conical crown. The annual shoots are triangular and reddish-brown. The older twigs have greyish-brown bark, which, on the thicker branches and the trunks, gradually changes into a brown outer bark that peels off in fibres. The needles grow in whorls of three and are tough and sharply pointed, with grooved depressions and a white band, formed by a waxy coating. The yellow male flowers, similar to small cones, grow in small bunches in the needle axils (1). They are supported by two whorls of small, triangular scales. From the inconspicuous, green female flowers, resembling buds, grow succulent small cones of globular shape similar to berries. These are green at first, maturing only in the second year, and are then blackish-blue with a white bloom and contain three triangular seeds.

● Juniper grows on downs, rocks, heaths and in sandy pine groves. It prefers poor soils. It is particularly abundant on pastures where sheep graze, as they eat the fruits and distribute the seeds in their excrement. It is cultivated as an ornamental shrub in gardens and is a protected species in some countries.

It is cultivated from seed obtained from the mature fruits. Crush the dried fruits and soak the seed in water for 24 hours. Sow in early spring in trays. Prick out the seedlings into flower-pots and then into the place where they are to grow. Juniper flowers in April and May and the fruits ripen in September and October of the following year.

Collect fully ripe fruits when they are blackish-blue in colour and dry spread out in thin layers. The temperature must not exceed 35 °C (95 °F) during drying.

Juniper berries have diuretic properties, stimulate bile production and appetite and have a beneficial effect on digestion. They also check the reproduction of bacteria. Juniper is used as a culinary herb and gives gin its characteristic flavour. The oil, which irritates the skin, is pressed from the berries and used externally for treating some inflammatory skin complaints, and internally for treating flatulence. Juniper must never be given to children or to people suffering from acute kidney complaints.

Diuretic tea: boil 30 g (1 oz) crushed berries in 500 ml (18 fl oz) water for two minutes. Take in three doses during the day.

Laburnum anagyroides MEDIC.
Laburnum

Fabaceae

● This is a shrub or small tree 5–8 m (16–26 ft) in height, with smooth, brown-green bark. The shoots are silvery greyish-green and whitish-felted towards the ends, the older twigs tending towards brown. The buds are alternate and arranged in a spiral, oval and blunt and covered with silvery felty scales. The bud at the tip is larger than the lateral buds. The leaves are alternate and trifoliate, being formed of elongated, entire leaflets with silvery hairs on the underside. The hermaphrodite, symmetrical flowers grow in groups of 10–30 in drooping, 10–20 cm (4–8 in) long racemes. They have a short, bell-shaped, two-lipped, five-toothed calyx covered with appressed hair. The corolla is five-petalled, golden yellow, the topmost and largest petal (the standard) having brown spots. The 10 stamens are fused by the filaments in a single bundle and bear orange anthers. The pistil is white-felted and curved and has a superior ovary. The fruits are flattened, rough pods (1) with silky hair, containing dark brown, kidney-shaped seeds.

● Laburnum is native to southern and western Europe and is widely cultivated in parks and gardens as an ornamental tree. It flowers from April to May and is poisonous.

It propagates very easily from seed, which matures in September and October. It flourishes best in light soils with a sufficient calcium content. It tolerates drought and frost well and grows very quickly. In its native habitats it grows most in upland deciduous woods. It easily escapes from cultivation in central and northern Europe.

The inflorescence and the leaves are dried in the shade in thin layers. The seeds are shelled from the mature pods and the drying process is completed in the shade.

Laburnum was once widely used in popular healing. It is no longer and, as it is poisonous, it should never be used in home medicines. A tranquillizing tea was prepared from the flowers and leaves, or leaves only, for treating nervous illnesses and mental disorders, such as melancholia and hysteria, as well as for treating migraine, arsenical poison-ing, liver complaints and asthma. The active constituents affect the spinal cord and the locomotion and respiratory centres, at first as a stimulant and then as a depressant. They increase blood pressure and also affect heart activity. Symptoms of Laburnum poisoning are vomiting, diarrhoea, cold sweating and, later, depression, fatigue, twitching of the muscles, spasms and dilation of the pupils. Sometimes poisoning is accompanied by sleepiness or hallucinations and delirium. In cases of severe poisoning, death can occur quickly.

1

Lamium album L.
White Dead-nettle

Labiatae

● White Dead-nettle is a perennial herb, 30—50 cm (12—20 in) tall. It has a richly branched, slender rhizome and erect, unbranched, hairy or almost glabrous stems, which are often violet and swollen at the bottom. The leaves are opposite, the lower ones being long- and the upper ones short-stalked. They are oval, with either a heart-shaped indentation or rounded at the stalk, pointed at the tip and coarsely toothed on the margin. The blade is covered with glandular hairs over the whole surface, which exude the substance that gives the plant its characteristic smell. Clusters of sessile flowers grow from the axils of upper leaves. They have a bell-shaped, half-open calyx divided into five tapering teeth, and a symmetrical, white or slightly yellowish, two-lipped corolla with a curved tube. Inside the corolla there are two long and two short stamens with dark brown anthers. The superior ovary has two compartments with two seeds in each, so that four black nutlets develop from these after maturing.

● White Dead-nettle is a common weed in woods, shady gardens, hedges, ditches, and on disturbed grounds. It grows on lowlands and uplands.

Collect the corollas in dry weather, placing them gently in a thickly woven basket. Dry as quickly as possible in the shade. If artificial heat is used, the temperature should not exceed 40 °C (104 °F). Neither during drying, nor during later storage should the plant turn brown or become damp. Therefore, store it particularly carefully, taking care not to squash it, in well-sealed tins. Collection is a time-consuming job.

The pharmaceutical industry uses extracts of White Dead-nettle in medicinal teas. It has tranquillizing, weak astringent and haemostatic properties and facilitates expectoration. It may also be used as a mouth rinse or gargle for sore throats and gums, in compresses and baths for suppurating wounds, haemorrhoids, eczema and burns. It is used to treat gynaecological disorders, for discharges and menstrual difficulties and to regulate intestinal activity and bowel movement. In France, an extract made from 20 g ($\frac{3}{4}$ oz) leaves in 1 litre ($1\frac{3}{4}$ pints) water is taken internally for cleansing the kidneys and to treat dropsy, intestinal haemorrhaging and blood in the urine. It is also used externally for some skin diseases.

Expectorant extract: scald 10 g ($\frac{2}{5}$ oz) dried flowers in 250 ml (9 fl oz) hot water. Take during the day in 5 ml (1 teaspoon) doses.

Larix decidua MILL.
European Larch

Pinaceae

● This conifer grows to a height of 30—40 m (98—131 ft). It has a conical crown when young, later irregularly oval. The yellowish-brown bark, smooth when young, changes after 10 years into slightly cracked outer bark and, when old, into a thick, corky, reddish-brown outer bark, fissured lengthwise. The annual shoots have brownish-yellow bark, and are glabrous and slender. The buds are small and ovately globular. The bud at the tip often sheds resin. The deciduous, 15—30 mm ($\frac{1}{2}$—1 in) long needles are arranged in a spiral on the annual shoots and on the older twigs they are clustered in groups of 25—40 on the barrel-shaped, shortened lateral twigs. These are soft and light green, flat or slightly arched at the top, with a prominent keel on the underside. The flowers are unisexual and the plant monoecious. The male flowers are in drooping, oval sulphur yellow clusters (1). The female inflorescences are erect, dark red, small and oval (2). The cones are oval and light brown, the seeds light brown and winged.

● This tree is native to the Alps and the Carpathians, but it is widely cultivated in woods and as an ornamental tree in parks and gardens. It flowers from April to June, depending on altitude. It flourishes in damp and deep soils and is completely frost-resistant. It grows very quickly when young; the saplings may be planted when only two years old.

Collect the annual shoots with the young needles in the spring months and use them fresh. At one time, Venetian turpentine was obtained from the European Larch by drilling the trunks and distilling the resin, which collected in openings temporarily plugged with stoppers. However, this damaged the trees. Turpentine can be obtained without causing damage by distilling from deadwood after winter felling. This technique has not been sufficiently exploited.

The turpentine is processed industrially into ointments for treating rheumatism and into inhalations for treating inflammatory conditions of the respiratory passages, as it has disinfec-tant effects against bacteria. In popular healing, steam is inhaled from a hot decoction made from the fresh annual shoots to relieve accumulated phlegm in the respiratory passages.

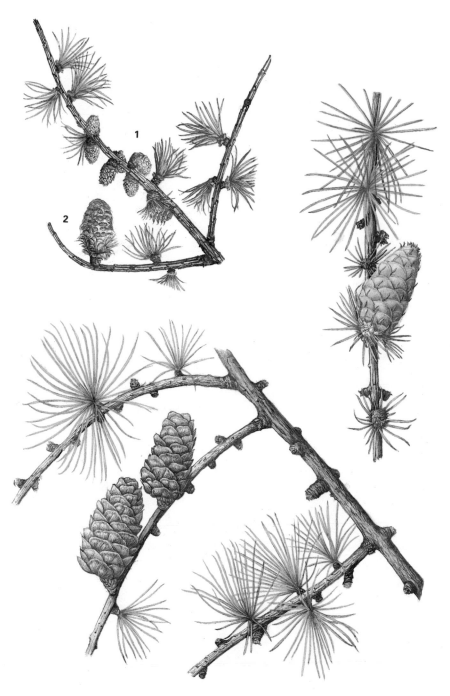

Lavandula angustifolia MILL.
Garden Lavender

 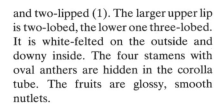

Labiatae

● This sub-shrub grows up to 60 cm (24 in) tall and forms richly branched tufts with erect branches. Square branches grow from the lower, woody, ascending parts of the stems. The leaves are opposite, without petioles, linear, entire with inrolled edges, bluntly pointed, grey-felted when young and later greyish-green with dot-like glands underneath. The flowers grow at the tops of the branches in groups of 5−10 in the axils of small bracts, and are arranged in spikes which are sparser in the lower part and denser above. They have a bluish-grey, tubular calyx, which spreads slightly into a funnel shape at the top. It is hairy and divided into five teeth; four of them are very short, the fifth being enlarged, oval, blunt and lobed. The corolla is symmetrical, blue and two-lipped (1). The larger upper lip is two-lobed, the lower one three-lobed. It is white-felted on the outside and downy inside. The four stamens with oval anthers are hidden in the corolla tube. The fruits are glossy, smooth nutlets.

● Garden Lavender is native to the Mediterranean and is cultivated elsewhere as an ornamental and melliferous plant. It is cultivated in large quantities for the manufacture of scent and for pharmaceutical purposes. It flowers from June to September.

It is propagated from seeds, cuttings or by dividing clumps. The plants require warm, light, permeable soils rich in calcium and a sheltered position in the sun. Prepare the soil to a depth of at least 40 cm (16 in). Sow the seed in February and March in sandy, humous soil in frames. Plant out in July in rows 20 cm (8 in) apart. Thin the plants in the autumn. Take cuttings from one-year-old shoots in spring and, when they have taken root, plant in cold frames at a distance of 40 cm (16 in) apart.

Collect the flower-bearing branches and dry them in bundles at a temperature of up to 35 °C (95 °F). Pull off the dry flowers and remove the twigs and leaves. If you are not going to use the flowers immediately, store them in well-sealed containers.

The flowers can be made into a tranquillizing tea for treating spasms, attacks of hysteria and flatulence. Lavender also stimulates the digestive tract and the infiltration of bile into the duodenum and has diuretic and antibacterial properties. An extract can be applied externally to improve circulation to the skin and as an antiseptic on various inflammations. It is used in medicinal cosmetics and in the manufacture of scents.

1

Extract for nervous problems: infuse 10−15 ml (2−3 teaspoons) flowers in 400 ml (14 fl oz) hot water. Take every other day.

VI–IX

Leonurus cardiaca L.
Motherwort

Labiatae

● Motherwort is a nasty-smelling perennial herb. It has a stout, branched rhizome. The stems are erect, 50–150 cm (20–59 in) tall, richly branched, square in cross-section and covered with spreading hair or almost glabrous. The leaves are opposite, stalked, oval, sometimes having a slight heart-shaped indentation at the stalk, and palmately divided into five to seven pointed lobes, which are coarsely toothed at the edges. The blade is covered with dense hair on the underside. In the upper part of the stem, the leaves gradually change into more simple, oval, tapering bracts, which narrow in a wedge shape towards the petiole. In the axils of the central and upper leaves and bracts there are tufts of sessile flowers with awl-shaped bracts. They have a tubular, funnel-shaped calyx divided into five tough, spiky teeth. The corolla is pink and finely hairy, and is only slightly longer than the calyx, with the upper lip shallowly vaulted and long-haired. The lower lip is shorter and divided into three lobes with brown spots. The stamens have hairy filaments. The fruits are brown nutlets.

● Motherwort grows in dry meadows, pastures, along waysides, on dumping grounds, in hedgerows, on embankments and in similar places. It flowers from June to September and is a melliferous plant.

Motherwort is an old medicinal plant used in popular healing for heart complaints. Collect flowering haulms and dry, hung in small bundles, in the shade.

It has diuretic properties and beneficial effects on hardened arteries, milder forms of Basedow's disease and high blood pressure. An extract or decoction may be taken to treat mild and chronic heart and blood vessel complaints, chiefly in the elderly, incipient sclerosis of the coronary vessels, an overworked heart caused by an accelerated pulse rate, and disorders of heart rhythm, as it slightly slows the pulse rate and reinforces the activity of the heart muscle. It has tranquillizing effects on the nervous system, and may be beneficial particularly in the case of changes in nervous activity accompanying ageing. It is also used to treat prostate in the elderly. Anti-spasmodic properties have also been discovered. It is more efficient in lowering blood pressure than Valerian, and the vitamin A and C content also has a beneficial effect.

Extract with tranquillizing properties: infuse 10 ml (2 teaspoons) dried haulm in 500 ml (18 fl oz) cold water. Take once a day.

105

Levisticum officinale KOCH
Lovage

Umbelliferae

V–VIII
VIII–IX

● This perennial, robust plant grows to a height of up to 200 cm (79 in). From the juicy, short, thick rhizome (1) long, richly branched roots grow. They are white inside and very aromatic. The basal leaves are up to 50 cm (20 in) in length, on long stalks and two to three times pinnate. The stalk is round, hollow and glabrous. The deep green, glossy leaflets are oval, narrowing into a wedge shape towards the base, coarsely toothed in the front or divided into two or three lobes. The stem is round, finely furrowed and branched at the top. The stem leaves are alternate, either on short stalks or sessile, pinnately divided or undivided. From the axils of the stem leaves grow branches bearing large, dense umbels consisting of 12–20 umbellets. The floral envelopes often form numerous tapering, white-bordered, toothed, rough bracts. The umbel stalks are thick and angled. The flowers have an inconspicuous calyx, and a corolla consisting of five pale yellow petals which are shallowly indented at the tips, and five stamens, the filaments of which bend towards the inside. The fruits are flat, yellow-brown double achenes with three prominent ribs on the ridge and bordered by narrow wings at the sides.

● Lovage is native to southern Europe, and is often cultivated as a vegetable or culinary herb, mainly in upland regions. It flowers in July and August. It flourishes in light, deep soils rich in calcium.

It is propagated either by means of the achenes or by rhizome cuttings. In the first year, only basal leaves grow. Cut off the inflorescences as they appear, in order to strengthen the underground parts.

Dig up the rhizomes with the roots the second or third year in August and September. Clean, rinse with water, cut in half lengthwise and dry with artificial heat at a temperature of up to 35 °C (95 °F). The dried rhizomes can easily become damp and mouldy and may be attacked by insects. Store in well-sealed tins. The fresh or dried leaves are also used in popular healing.

A decoction made from fresh or dried leaves has diuretic properties and may be taken to treat inflammation of the bladder and urinary tract and to stimulate bile excretion. A decoction made from the dried roots can help relieve bronchitis. For loss of appetite, a pinch of powder made from the dried root may be taken three times daily before meals. A decoction made from the roots or fresh haulms may be used to bathe inflamed skin and as a bath additive.

Decoction for bronchitis: boil 15 g ($\frac{1}{2}$ oz) crushed dried root in 250 ml (9 fl oz) water for three minutes. Take three times a day.

Alcohol extract for improving the appetite: macerate 25 g ($\frac{4}{5}$ oz) Lovage rhizome and 3 g ($\frac{1}{10}$ oz) Valerian root in 100 ml (3 $\frac{1}{2}$ fl oz) spirit for three days. Take 10 drops three times a day.

Linaria vulgaris MILL.
Common Toadflax

Scrophulariaceae

● This is a perennial herb with stems 20–50 cm (8–20 in) in height. It has a slender, creeping, branched, woody rhizome, simple, vertical small roots and smooth, cylindrical, erect, simple or branched stems. The stem leaves are dense, alternate, sessile, narrowly tapering to linear, entire, slightly inrolled at the edges and pointed, with a single nerve. The stalked flowers grow from the bract axils in a conical raceme which gradually lengthens during flowering. The glabrous calyx, which is shorter than the flower stalk, is divided into five oval, pointed tips. The corolla is symmetrical, two-lipped, mostly lemon yellow with an orange centre, and elongated towards the base into a conical spur. Inside the corolla four stamens are hidden, a pistil with a globular to oval superior ovary and a stigma which broadens into a club shape and is split at the tip. The ovary matures into an oval capsule (1) with dark brown, kidney-shaped seeds.

● Common Toadflax grows in fields and pastures, on waste ground, grasslands and rocks, and as a weed in gardens. It occurs on lowlands and uplands. It flowers from June to September.

The flowering haulm has medicinal properties. Cut off the flowering tops of the stems and dry them in the shade in bundles.

Common Toadflax has been used since the earliest times as a laxative, diuretic, fever-reducing and anti-inflammatory medicine. There is evidence that it stimulates the activity of smooth muscles in the digestive tract and uterus and increases the flow of bile through the bile-duct. Applied externally, it has beneficial effects on varicose veins, particularly haemorrhoids. It was once prescribed in cases of persis-tent constipation, insufficient supply of bile and other disorders of the digestive tract, for flatulence and for negative reactions to fat in the diet. A decoction made from Common Toadflax, Cornflower, Eyebright and Chamomile may be used on compresses to treat inflamed skin and bruises. If the decoction is properly sterilized, it may be used as drops to treat conjunctivitis and other eye infections. Common Toadflax is not recommended for use on its own; it is usually combined with other plants with compatible properties.

Paste compress for varicose veins, haemorrhoids and skin rashes: scald 20 g ($\frac{3}{4}$ oz) drug in 500 ml (18 fl oz) milk.

107

Linum usitatissimum L.
Flax

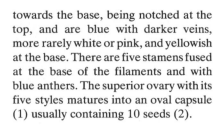

VIII

Linaceae

● Flax is an annual herb up to 100 cm (39 in) tall. An erect stem grows from the long slender root. The stem is sparsely to richly branched in the upper part, rounded and densely leafed. The leaves are narrow, alternate, sessile, simple, entire, bractless and glabrous. The lower ones are tapering to linear and pointed. In the central part of the stem the leaves are larger, ending in a spiny point, and coloured greyish-green. The hermaphrodite, regular, pentamerous flowers are arranged in panicles composed of rich, loose monochasia growing on erect stalks which are longer than the calyx. The sepals are oval with a sharp keel, short-pointed, glabrous, hairy on the front edge, and have a broad, dry membranous border. The petals narrow into a wedge shape towards the base, being notched at the top, and are blue with darker veins, more rarely white or pink, and yellowish at the base. There are five stamens fused at the base of the filaments and with blue anthers. The superior ovary with its five styles matures into an oval capsule (1) usually containing 10 seeds (2).

● The original wild plant is not known. Flax has been cultivated for its fibre and its seeds for more than 5,000 years in Europe and Asia. It frequently escapes from cultivation, although usually only temporarily. It flowers from June to August and is slightly poisonous. It is cultivated as a textile plant predominantly in mountain regions, in the Alps up to altitudes of 1,800 metres (6,000 ft) above sea level. At lower altitudes it is grown mostly for the production of linseed oil; the seeds contain up to 40 per cent of this.

The seeds are either used directly or the linseed oil is pressed from them. An extract with laxative properties may be made from both the fresh and the dried flowering haulm. Linseeds ground in water may be taken internally to treat digestive disorders and to cleanse the intestines, at the same time checking the reproduction of pathogenic intestinal micro-organisms. Finely crushed and mixed with a small quantity of warm water to make a paste, linseed can be applied as a hot poultice on abscesses, where it speeds up suppuration. A decoction made from the seeds may be used as a gargle or mouth rinse to treat sore throats and gums and taken internally for bronchial catarrh. It also forms part of diabetic teas.

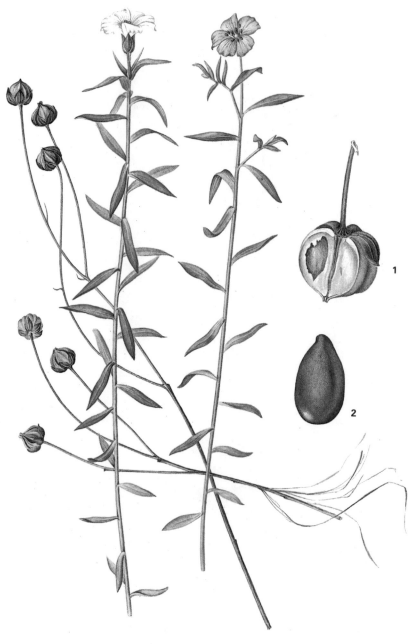

1

2

Decoction for bronchial catarrh: boil 10 g ($\frac{2}{5}$ oz) seeds in 400 ml (14 fl oz) water for 15 minutes, sweeten with honey and take 5 ml (1 teaspoon) every two hours.

108

Malva sylvestris L.
Common Mallow

Malvaceae

● Common Mallow is a biennial to perennial herb with stems 120–150 cm (47–59 in) in height. It has a thick, spindle-shaped root with numerous lateral rootlets. In the first year, a rosette of long-stalked basal leaves grows. These are palmately lobed three to seven times, rounded with round or oval to triangular lobes which are toothed at the edges. At the stalk they are straight or with shallow heart-shaped indentations and irregularly toothed at the edges. The blade is sparsely hairy, the hairs being denser along the nerves and on the stalk, growing both individually and in bunches. The erect stem sometimes turns woody at the base, branches richly from the bottom upwards and is covered with hairs. In the axils of the alternate stem leaves grow long-stalked flowers in groups of two to six. They have an epicalyx consisting of loose, longish tapering leaflets and a calyx joined up to two-thirds of its length. The pale pink to violet-purple corolla with darker small veins is formed of five indented petals. The dotted, flat fruits (1) fall apart into 15–18 seeds (2).

● Common Mallow grows in dry meadows and pastures, on waste land and roadsides. It flourishes mainly in warmer regions and flowers from June to September.

Collect the flowers (without stalks) in dry weather, ideally about' noon. As they fade quickly and new flowers are constantly opening, it is best to collect them every other day. Dry in the shade at a temperature of up to 40 °C (104 °F). They darken during drying to a bluish violet colour. The leaves also have medicinal properties. Collect only the largest leaves, together with the stalks, before they have started to with-

er. Only quite healthy leaves without rusty spots or other impurities are suitable. Dry them in a similar manner to the flowers. They should remain green. Store in well-sealed containers.

The plants can be grown from seed. Sow either immediately after maturing in autumn or in spring in April. Nowadays, the related species, *Malva mauritiana*, is more frequently cultivated for pharmaceutical purposes.

Common Mallow is anti-inflammatory, mildly astringent and phlegm-dispersing. It also helps alleviate the irritant properties of other medicines. It may be taken to treat various defects of the gastric and intestinal mucous membranes and has absorptive properties, similar to those of medicinal charcoal. An extract or decoction may be prepared to improve expectoration in cases of bronchitis and hoarseness, and a double concentration may be used as a gargle.

Extract for use as an expectorant and gargle: scald 10–15 g ($\frac{2}{3}$–$\frac{1}{2}$ oz) dried flowers in 500 ml (18 fl oz) boiling water and take in doses of 100 ml ($3\frac{1}{2}$ oz), two to four times daily.

Expectorant extract: macerate 5 ml (1 teaspoon) dried leaves in 100 ml ($3\frac{1}{2}$ fl oz) cold water.

Marrubium vulgare L.
White Horehound

Labiatae

● White Horehound is a perennial herb with a stout rhizome. Ascending, 30–50 cm (12–20 in) tall stems are branched at the top, square, hollow, densely felted when young and later sparsely covered in white woolly hair. They bear opposite, stalked, broadly oval to heart-shaped leaves, which are finely felted on the upper side and grey to white-felted on the underside. The blades are wrinkled along the veins, and coarsely toothed at the edges. In the lower part of the stem, the leaves are long-stalked, in the upper part the stalks are shorter. Dense semi-globular small clusters of tiny flowers grow from the leaf axils. The calyx (1) is tubular, white-felted, and, up to a third or even a half of its length, divided into six to ten teeth which are glabrous, tough, and later bent downwards into a hook. The corolla is white, downy, symmetrical and two-lipped (2). The lower lip is divided into three lobes; the central lobe is three times longer than the lateral ones. The upper lip is deeply incised into two pointed lobes and is much narrower. There are four stamens. The fruits are four smooth, oval nutlets, which are enclosed in the calyx during the period of maturity.

● White Horehound originates from southern Europe and has spread to grow elsewhere on roadsides, in hedges, in dry pastures and on dumping grounds. It grows on lowlands and uplands. It flowers from June to September.

It is not particularly demanding in cultivation, requiring light, permeable soil in dry, warm situations. Sow the seeds in April in rows 30 cm (12 in) apart. Thin out the seedlings to a distance of 20 cm (8 in) apart. It can also be propagated by dividing the clumps in October after harvesting. Weed and hoe the beds and apply fertilizer once a year.

Collect the whole haulm during the flowering period two or three times a year from July to September. Dry spread out in thin layers in the shade at a temperature of up to 40 °C (104 °F). Store in well-sealed containers. The powder from the dried haulm irritates the respiratory passages, so you are recommended to wear a mask over the mouth and nose when you are handling it.

Both the dried haulm and the fresh juice from the plant have been used since early times for treating bronchial catarrh and diarrhoea, and improving the appetite and bile production. When mixed with Valerian and Hawthorn, it has beneficial effects on the nervous system and on heart activity.

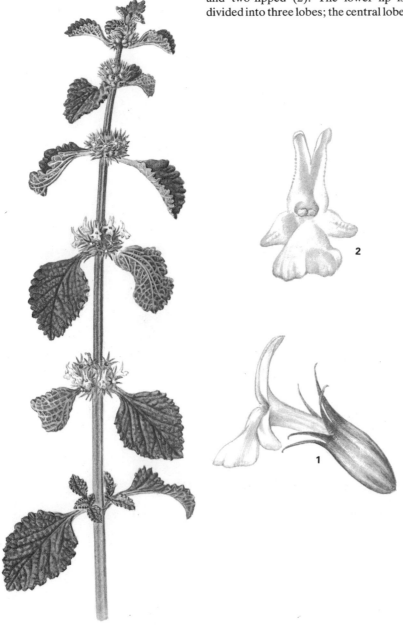

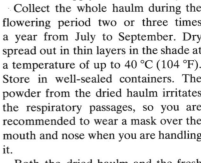

Extract for bronchial catarrh: infuse 10–30 g ($\frac{2}{3}$–1 oz) dried haulm in 400 ml (14 fl oz) water and drink in doses of 100 ml ($3\frac{1}{2}$ fl oz) three times a day.

Syrup: boil 100 g ($3\frac{1}{2}$ oz) dried haulm in 750 ml (26 fl oz) water. Strain and add 500 g (18 oz) sugar. Boil the mixture until it thickens.

Melilotus officinalis (L.) PALL
Ribbed Melilot

Leguminosae

● Ribbed Melilot is a biennial, more rarely an annual, stout herb. The ascending, 50–150 cm (20–59 in) tall stems grow from a spindle-shaped root. They are angled, glabrous or only with scattered hair at the top, branched and hollow. The leaves are alternate, sparse, long-stalked and trifoliate, with the central leaflet always on a long stalk and the lateral two on short ones. The leaflets are elongated, oval, pointed, toothed and glabrous with 6–13 pairs of lateral nerves. There are awl-shaped stipules situated at the leaf stalk. From the axils of the upper leaves grow single racemes of 30–70 stalked, drooping flowers (1). They are yellow at first but turn paler towards the end of flowering. The five-toothed calyx falls after flowering. The 10 stamens are joined into two bunches. The superior, glabrous ovary matures into oval, glabrous, wrinkled pods, which are bluntly terminated and brownish-grey to red at maturity. They contain one or two seeds.

● Ribbed Melilot grows in pastures, on rocky slopes, waste land, roadside and railway embankments, dumping grounds and other abandoned places on lowlands and uplands. It flowers from May to September. It has no special soil requirements, but does best in dry soils with a sufficient calcium content. Sow the seeds in rows 30–40 cm (12–16 in) apart in autumn or spring.

Collect the haulm from June to September. Cut off the flower-bearing tops, 20–25 cm (8–10 in) long, with a knife or scissors. Dry in small bundles in the shade or spread in thin layers at a temperature of up to 35 °C (95 °F). Store in well-sealed containers.

Ribbed Melilot is used mainly for compresses and for bathing wounds.

A decoction or an extract made with cold water is used for treating varicose veins, haemorrhoids, vein inflammation accompanied by swelling of the lower limbs, and ulcerated legs. It also alleviates rheumatic pain. It should not be taken internally as a home medicine as it contains coumarin which acts as a narcotic. Larger doses cause headaches, dizziness and retching.

Mentha crispa (L.) BENTH.
Crisped Mint

Labiatae

● Crisped Mint is a perennial aromatic herb 50–70 cm (20–28 in) tall. It has a richly branched, creeping, white, slender underground rhizome. Numerous ascending stems, square in cross section, are covered with rough, bristly hair. The alternate leaves are oval, pointed at the ends, either on very short stalks or sessile, and with slight heart-shaped indentations or only divided at the stalk. The blade is dark green on the upper side and greyish-green on the underside, with coarse prominent veins and 6–10 pairs of lateral nerves. The edge of the leaf extends into long, sharply pointed corrugated teeth. Dot-like glands are visible on the blade. Non-flowering lateral twigs occasionally grow from the axils of the lower leaves. Clusters of flowers are produced from the axils of the upper leaves. They are arranged in interrupted terminal spikes with bracts and occur on the main stem as well as on the topmost branches. The bell-shaped, glabrous calyx is divided into three-sided pointed teeth. The corolla is reddish-violet and symmetrical (1). The fruits are four nutlets.

● Crisped Mint is thought to be a hybrid of Water Mint (*Mentha aquatica*) and Common Mint (*Mentha arvensis*). It is very variable. If closer to Water Mint, the terminal inflorescences prevail, while if it is more closely related to Common Mint, clusters of flowers in the leaf axils prevail. It flowers from July to September.

It is cultivated in gardens, occasionally turning wild in hedgerows, ditches and rubbish heaps. It flourishes in damp, shady, warm places with humous soil. It is propagated either by division of the clumps in spring and autumn, or from stem cuttings from the non-flowering twigs or the stem tips in spring, planted at 50 cm (20 in) apart in rows 30 cm (12 in) apart. Propagation from seeds is not recommended, because the seedlings have dissimilar characteristics, both in appearance and in medicinal properties.

Cut the stems and pull off the leaves. Sort, clean and dry immediately in the shade. Store in well-sealed containers.

Crisped Mint may be used as a substitute for Peppermint to treat gastric problems and diarrhoea, improve the appetite, as a carminative and for gallbladder complaints, as it stimulates bile production. Mint tea is a pleasant drink and the leaves are also added to liqueurs for flavouring.

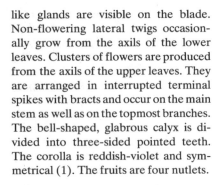

1

Extract for gastric problems, flatulence and diarrhoea: scald 15 ml (1 tablespoon) dried leaves in 500 ml (18 fl oz) boiling water and take three times a day.

Mentha piperita L.
Peppermint

Labiatae

● The characteristic smell of this perennial herb is caused by its high menthol content. It has a creeping rhizome which turns woody with age. The erect, 30–60 cm (12–24 in) tall, square stems are usually branched at the top and hairy, particularly along the edges. The lower part of the stem is swollen and coloured violet. The oval leaves are tapering, opposite, stalked, pointed at the ends, only slightly hairy or glabrous and irregularly and sharply toothed at the edge. The blade is dotted with glands, with prominent main and lateral small veins on the underside. The flowers (1) grow in small clusters in the axils of the upper leaves and bracts. At the tips of the stem and branches dense, cylindrical spikes are formed. The flowers have a tubular, curved calyx, glabrous in the lower part and divided into five teeth bordered with bristly hairs. Only the tip of the symmetrical, pale purple corolla protrudes from the calyx, which is divided into four tips which turn backwards. The four stamens have glabrous filaments. The pistil has a superior ovary and a divided stigma which protrudes conspicuously from the corolla. The fruits, brown oval nutlets, rarely develop.

● Peppermint is thought to be a hybrid of Water Mint (*Mentha aquatica*) and Spearmint (*Mentha spicata*). There are numerous cultivated varieties and it occasionally turns wild in ditches and along the banks of streams, usually from broken-off pieces washed up from gardens or discarded on rubbish heaps. It flowers from July to September.

It flourishes in damp soils with a sufficient calcium content and on gravelly or sandy deposits with an admixture of loam. The essential oil content greatly depends on soil and climatic conditions. Adequate light is particularly important. Propagate in early spring from stem cuttings, not from seed.

Collect the leaves (usually twice a year) or the whole flowering stem. Dry in the shade at a temperature of up to 35 °C (95 °F).

Peppermint has beneficial effects on the nervous system, relieves pain, regulates the activity of the digestive system, stimulates the appetite and gallbladder activity and is carminative, with generally reviving effects. It is refreshing and so makes a good substitute for tea. Peppermint tea should not be drunk exclusively, as with long-term use, it irritates the kidneys. The fresh crushed leaves may be placed on the forehead to relieve headaches.

Tea: scald 5 g ($\frac{1}{5}$ oz) dried leaves in 500 ml (18 fl oz) water and take once a day.

Decoction as a gargle and mouth rinse: scald 10 g ($\frac{2}{5}$ oz) dried leaves in 250 ml (9 fl oz) water.

113

Menyanthes trifoliata L.
Bogbean

Gentianaceae

● This is a perennial, aquatic plant 15—30 cm (6—12 in) tall. It has a thick, creeping, branched rhizome, which is jointed, scaly and coloured green, dirty white or brownish. Brown, small cylindrical roots grow from this and at the joints, there are small bunches of small, fine hair-like roots. At the ends of the rhizome branches, which tend upwards, large trifoliate leaves grow on long stalks. They are glabrous, entire, with rather a thick blade. The leaflets are large, oval and blunt-ended. The leaf stalk broadens in the lower part. Next to the leaves grow leafless stalks bearing at the tip a cluster of light pink flowers. These grow on stalks from the axils of small bracts and are regular and hermaphrodite. The calyx is divided into five blunt points and the broadly funnel-shaped corolla (1) to about a half of its length into five fringed tips covered with white hairs. There are five stamens with violet anthers. The superior ovary is composed of two carpels. The style terminates in a club-shaped stigma. The fruit is an oval capsule.

● Bogbean grows in bogs, peat-bogs, fens, ditches, shallow pools and on wet meadows, flourishing in lowlands and uplands. With the drying-out of bogs and the draining and reclamation of meadows, however, it is rapidly disappearing from the countryside. Consequently, it is a protected species in many countries. It flowers in May and June.

It can be cultivated in places comparable with its natural environment and in artificial ponds. Propagation is by dividing the rhizomes.

Collect the leaves with a small part of the stalk either during flowering or after the flowers have faded. Cut carefully, as, in boggy soil, it is easy to pull up the plant with the roots as well. Dry the leaves spread out in thin layers with artificial heat. They dry poorly but the drying should be as quick as possible so that they do not turn black. Discard any discoloured leaves.

Bogbean helps to improve the appetite and is used to treat digestive disorders and a lack of gastric juices. It may be used on its own or in a blend with other medicinal plants. It is mildly laxative and is also said to have beneficial effects on the nervous system. It is a tonic for the whole body, so it is helpful in cases of physical exhaustion, debility and during convalescence. It has a very bitter taste.

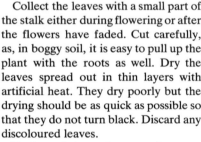

1

Decoction for digestive disorders and for improving the appetite: boil 10 g ($\frac{2}{3}$ oz) dried leaves in 250 ml (9 fl oz) water for three minutes. Take half in the morning and the other half in the evening.

Stomach drops: steep 30 g (1 oz) dried leaves in 125 ml ($4\frac{1}{2}$ fl oz) distilled liquor for one week. Take 10 drops three times daily before meals.

V–VII

VIII

V–X

Myrrhis odorata (L.) Scop.
Sweet Cicely

Umbelliferae

● A perennial plant with a brown, many-headed, branched rhizome. The stem is erect, 50–120 cm (20–47 in) in height, rounded, finely furrowed when dry, hollow, branched in the upper part and partly covered with fine hairs. The leaves are soft, pale green and, particularly when young, covered in fine greyish hair. The lower ones are long-stalked and the upper ones sessile. The stalks broaden at the base into a boat-shaped, slightly enclosing sheath. The blade is broadly three-sided in contour and two to three times finely pinnate, divided into irregular sections which extend at the tip into a point, with sparsely toothed edges. The inflorescences in dense compound umbels without envelopes grow at the tips of the branches. The five to seven tapering, pointed bracts spread out from the stalks in a bowl shape. The flowers are borne on finely felted or glabrous stalks. Some of them are only male, others are hermaphrodite. The white petals are heart-shaped and larger at the edges of the umbellets. The fruits are black, conical, glossy achenes (1). The whole plant has a strong smell.

● Sweet Cicely grows throughout western and southern Europe. It used to be widely cultivated in many places in Europe and has turned wild or naturalized especially in upland meadows, riverside hedgerows, and on roadsides. It is very common in northern Britain. It does particularly well in soils rich in calcium, and flowers from May to July.

Collect the haulm shortly before flowering, and the fruits and roots during flowering. Dry in the shade by natural heat or by artificial heat at temperatures up to 40 °C (104 °F).

Sweet Cicely is rarely used as a medicinal herb nowadays. The crushed fresh haulm may be placed on painful areas caused by gout and on rheumatic joints. The dried haulm is sometimes smoked instead of tobacco, as it is said to facilitate expectoration. Otherwise, it may be taken internally for asthma and breathlessness caused by lung problems. The fresh juice from the pulverized root can be used for the same purpose. In the past, the plant was said to be an effective 'blood cleanser'. An extract made from the root and fruits used to be taken to treat sore throats and chest pains as well as bladder disorders. The plant is believed to stimulate milk production and, therefore, used to be used in veterinary medicine. An alcohol extract made from the fruits and rhizomes was a favourite medicine for gastric discomfort and digestive problems. Tea made from the dry haulm was taken to promote sleep.

1

115

Nasturtium officinale R. Br.
Watercress

V–IX

Brassicaceae

● This is a perennial herb. The small root of the seedling soon dies off and a branched, creeping rhizome with numerous small bunches of secondary roots forms in its place. The ascending stems, 20–90 cm (8–35 in) tall, are angularly furrowed, hollow, densely leafy and often branched. They take root at the base. The leaves are alternate, odd-pinnate, rather thick, fresh green in colour and composed of round to oval leaflets which are either entire or bluntly indented with teeth at the edges. The terminal leaflet is usually larger, being round or heart-shaped, bent like a spoon, with a wavy, toothed edge. The bractless flowers grow in racemes at the stem tips. They have an open calyx consisting of four elongated sepals and a white corolla of four oval petals which are flat and open in the upper part, narrowing visibly towards the base, and entire. The stamens are shorter than the corolla and have yellow anthers. After fading, the raceme elongates and from the pistils develop slender, often sickle-shaped pods which are curved upwards and contain seeds in two rows.

● Watercress grows at springs, along the banks of streams with clear water and, more rarely, in clear still water. It flowers from May to August, sometimes for a second time in October. It can also be cultivated in winter at home in a similar manner to cress. Sow the seeds in bowls of wet sand and keep them damp. They soon germinate and the seedlings may then be eaten in salads. Watercress has a pungent and slightly bitter taste.

The flowering haulm has medicinal properties. A reviving tea with diuretic properties may be prepared. This may also be taken in cases of digestive disorders, stimulating the appetite and the production of gastric juices and having mild laxative effects. In Romania, fresh juice from the plant is added to milk and syrups and applied externally to treat skin complaints. In France, a syrup is prepared from the fresh juice. Watercress is also used to treat dropsy, kidney inflammation, liver diseases, intestinal disorders, fatigue, bronchitis and other lung diseases. Compresses made from the crushed fresh leaves and stalks may be placed on skin complaints. In popular healing in Poland, the plant is used to treat diabetes and poor gallbladder activity. Fresh Watercress, rich in vitamins A, C and D, is recommended for vitamin deficiency.

Syrup: simmer 500 ml (18 fl oz) fresh juice and 750 g (1 lb 10 oz) sugar over low heat.

116

Ononis spinosa L.
Spiny Rest-harrow

Fabaceae

● This semi-shrub, 30–60 cm (12–24 in) in height, has a long, very tough, woody root. The reddish, swollen stems, which turn woody at the base, are usually richly branched with hairy, thorny twigs. The alternate leaves are trimerous in the lower part of the plant and in the upper part simple with oval, glandularly hairy, finely toothed deciduous leaflets. The large toothed bracts are joined to the stalk. The symmetrical, bisexual flowers grow in sparse racemes from the leaf axils. The calyx, divided into five lobes, is glandular and covered with long hair. The corolla is rich pink or even white. There are 10 stamens. The superior ovary, with a single cell, develops into a pod swollen into a pouch and terminating in an awl-shaped small beak which bends downwards. It is oval in shape, yellowish-brown, covered with glandular hairs and situated in a permanent calyx which opens into a bell shape when the pod has formed. It usually contains two, sometimes even three, rough, brown seeds.

● Spiny Rest-harrow grows on sunny, dry slopes, in pastures, along waysides, on ridges and rocky slopes, particularly in calcereous or clay slates on lowlands and uplands. It flowers from June to September.

Dig up the roots of plants which are several years old, in September and October. Remove the aerial parts and the slender, branched roots, so that only the rhizome remains with the thicker, slightly branched roots. Rinse thoroughly with water and cut thick roots in half lengthwise. Dry in thin layers in the shade at a temperature of up to 50 °C (122 °F). The correctly dried rhizome is crumbly. In popular healing, the whole dried or fresh flowering haulm is also used.

The dried root has diuretic properties, stimulates digestion and bile production and is an expectorant. It is also effective against inflammation of the digestive tract and of the urinary system. In popular healing, an extract made with boiling water is used to treat high blood pressure and rheumatism and to disinfect the urinary tract. It may also be applied externally to certain skin complaints. The haulm has similar uses and is also applied to slow-healing wounds. The root is added to medicinal tea blends.

Extract with diuretic properties: infuse 15 g ($\frac{1}{2}$ oz) crushed root in 200 ml (7 fl oz) boiling water. Take in three doses during the day.

Origanum vulgare L.
Marjoram

VIII–IX

Labiatae

● This is a perennial herb with a slender, branched, woody root. The ascending, 20–50 cm (8–20 in) tall stems are square, hairy, leafy und usually reddish in colour. They are oppositely branched in the upper part and terminate in a rich dichasial inflorescence. The leaves are opposite, on short stalks, broadly oval, pointed or round at the ends, entire or slightly toothed and hairy at the edges. On the underside, they are lighter with transparent dot-like glands. The flowers grow in the axils of the sessile bracts, which are of the same shape as the leaves. The flowers grow on short stalks, in groups of one to three, and the whole inflorescence has an oval shape. The calyx (1) is symmetrical, divided into five lobes and has a tubular bell shape. As soon as the corolla falls and the fruits mature, it is enclosed by a ring of hairs. The two-lipped corolla (2) is light red, or, rarely, white in colour. The upper lip is erect and short, the lower one longer and divided into three points. The fruit is a nutlet.

● Marjoram grows in open woods and is common on dry grassland in the south. It flourishes on lowlands and uplands, occurring more abundantly in warmer regions. It flowers from July to September.

It is cultivated both from seed and by dividing the clumps. Sow the seed in frames in March or April. Plant out the seedlings 50 cm (20 in) apart in rows 30 cm (12 in) apart. Light, calcareous soils in a dry, warm location are the most suitable.

Collect the flowering haulm from August to September, in warmer places as early as July. Cut it off close to the ground and remove the thicker stalks. Plants are richest in essential oils if they are collected around midday. Dry spread out in thin layers in the shade or suspended in small bundles at a temperature of up to 35 ° C (95 ° F). Store in well-sealed containers.

Marjoram has disinfectant, anti-inflammatory and expectorant properties, and increases urine excretion. It is thought to be effective in treating spasms and nervous disorders such as depression, persistent coughs, whooping cough, diseases of the respiratory passages and loss of appetite. It is used to prepare tonic baths, particularly for small children, gargles for treating sore gums and coughs, and compresses for treating swollen glands. Inhaling the steam relieves coughs and colds. Marjoram is also a common culinary herb, known as oregano (the herb known as marjoram comes from the related species *Origanum majorana*).

II–VI

 V–VI

VIII–IX

Paeonia officinalis L.
Peony

Paeoniaceae

● The Peony is an ornamental, perennial herb 50–60 cm (20–24 in) in height, with spindle-shaped to cylindrical, thick, pulpy roots which taper at both ends. The basal leaves and simple stems, terminating in a single flower, grow from these. The leaves are bi- to trimerous, the central lobe having three to five sections, which are elongated to oval, entire and sometimes hairy on the underside. The plant is otherwise glabrous. The blade is dark green on the upper side, greyish to whitish green on the underside. The stem leaves are alternate. The flowers are large, purple-red, pink or white. Only the purple-red flowers of the double-flowering varieties in which almost all the stamens are transformed into petals are collected. In isolated instances, individual stamens with yellow anthers occur among these, or with the anther occurring on a transmuted corolla petal. From the two to three erect or slanting, glabrous or white-felted pistils develop pointed oval, swollen follicles which are bent outwards and contain shiny, bluish-black seeds.

● The Peony is native to southern and south-eastern Europe, where the wild form grows. In gardens it is cultivated predominantly in the double-flowered forms. It flowers in May and June. It can be easily propagated by dividing the clumps.

Collect the petals from the fading flowers shortly before they fall, when they will come away at a touch. Dry them quickly, spread out in thin layers so that they do not lose their colour.

Store in dark, dry conditions. The roots are also collected for medicinal purposes. Dig them up from February to April, clean thoroughly and dry whole and unpeeled by artificial heat. The seeds are also used on rare occasions. Dry them in the shade in natural heat and store in well-sealed containers.

Peony has anti-inflammatory and tranquillizing properties and also stimulates the production of gastric juices. It is widely used to treat kidney colic and kidney diseases. Peony is extensively used in popular healing. The root has anti-spasmodic properties and calms the nerves. The flower has similar properties and also forms part of anti-tussive teas. It is also used to colour some teas and syrups. A decoction made from the seeds may be taken to treat stomach spasms, diarrhoea and irregular menstruation.

Decoction for kidney stones: simmer 10 g ($\frac{2}{3}$ oz) dried petals in 250 ml (9 fl oz) water for one minute. Take 200 ml (7 fl oz) per dose.

Decoction for irregular menstruation: simmer 15 g ($\frac{1}{2}$ oz) chopped seeds in 250 ml (9 fl oz) water for five minutes. Take during the day in spoonfuls.

Papaver rhoeas L.
Common Poppy

Papaveraceae

● The Common Poppy is an annual herb up to 90 cm (35 in) in height. It has a slender, spindle-shaped root. The simple or sparsely branched stem is erect and has spreading bristles. The leaves are alternate and bristly, the lower ones narrowing into a petiole, the upper ones sessile, once to twice pinnately cut, with sharply toothed sections. The single flowers grow from the leaf axils on long, bristly stalks. They are often drooping when young and later erect, up to 10 cm (4 in) in diameter. The green calyx is composed of two boat-shaped sepals; they are bristly and soon fall. The petals are slender, entire and vivid red, often with a black blotch at the bottom in the centre. There is a large number of black stamens, which have slender, flat and unbroadened filaments. The pistil has a superior, oval ovary which is rounded at the base and has no style. A star-shaped stigma is situated directly on this. It is generally divided into 10 lobes. It matures into an oval, glabrous poppy head with kidney-shaped, dimpled seeds.

● The Common Poppy is a common lowland weed in fields, on dumping grounds and on road and railway embankments. It flourishes mainly in warmer areas and flowers from May to July.

Collect the petals from flowers which have just opened. Fading and fallen petals are of less value. Collect them in dry weather when there is no more dew, ideally around noon, and place them gently in a basket. Be careful not to squash them. Dry them as quickly as possible in the shade at a temperature of up to 40 °C (104 °C). The correctly dried petals should be a dingy reddish-violet colour and must not go black. Store in completely dry conditions in well-sealed containers.

Common Poppy has anti-tussive properties and is particularly recommended to people who cannot tolerate other medicines or when other treatments have not been effective. It also acts as a tranquillizer and contributes to sound sleep. The Polish pharmacopoeia recommends it for treating persistent coughs, sore throats and influenza in children and the elderly. It is quite often combined with an equal weight of Marsh Mallow root, Liquorice, Mullein and Mallow flowers to treat lung complaints. It is usually taken in the form of an extract made with hot water.

Syrup for children: macerate 100 g ($3 \frac{1}{2}$ oz) dried petals in 333 ml (12 fl oz) boiling distilled water with the juice of $\frac{1}{2}$ lemon for eight hours. Then add 2.5 kg ($5 \frac{1}{2}$ lb) sugar and simmer. The daily dose for children up to 15 months is 5 ml (1 teaspoon) syrup, for older children 10–30 ml (2–6 teaspoons).

Papaver somniferum L.
Opium Poppy

Papaveraceae

● This is an annual herb with a simple spindle-shaped taproot and a cylindrical, erect stem up to 100 cm (39 in) tall. It is simple or slightly branched, glabrous and blue with a white bloom. The leaves are alternate, with uneven indentations and a toothed margin. The lower leaves are on short stalks, the upper ones sessile to semi-enclosing and almost entire. The buds are drooping, becoming erect as they open. The flowers have a deciduous calyx consisting of two boat-shaped sepals and four large white, pink, red or violet colour petals, with a large, brownish-violet blotch at the bottom in the centre. The corolla is also very short-lived. There are many stamens, the filaments of which, with their grey anthers, broaden out into a club shape. A star-shaped stigma, divided into 8—12 pointed tips, is attached to the barrel-shaped, styleless superior ovary. The fruit (1) is a globular or oval, glabrous capsule. The seeds are grey or white, and dark blue in cultivated varieties.

● Opium Poppy originates from Asia Minor. It is cultivated for the oil from the seeds and as a medicinal plant. All the green parts of the plant, particularly the immature capsules, are supplied by latex tubes which exude a thick white liquid when cut.

After drying, it yields the drug known as opium. The plant flourishes in soils rich in calcium in sunny positions in regions where wheat thrives.

It is propagated from seed, which is sown in March in rows 30 cm (12 in) apart. The seedlings are then thinned to a distance of 25 cm (10 in). For the seed, varieties whose capsules do not open after maturing are cultivated. The seeds mature within six to eight weeks after the flowers have faded. The plants are cut off with a knife, with the stalks to a length of 10 cm (4 in) at most. The seeds, shaken out of the cut poppy heads, are left to finish drying in a thin layer and are kept in well-sealed containers. Opium Poppy cannot be grown without a licence and this is only granted for legitimate research or pharmaceutical purposes.

The seeds are used for cooking and baking, or the oil is pressed from them.

The empty poppy heads are processed by the pharmaceutical industry to obtain the alkaloids contained in opium. It is a powerful narcotic, reduces sensitivity to pain and induces sleep. It is used by the medical profession as a tranquillizer and painkiller, for treating persistent diarrhoea and as an anti-spasmodic. It also suppresses the urge to cough. As it alleviates pain and spasmodic contractions in smooth muscle, preparations made from opium alkaloids are also prescribed for gallbladder colic and similar ailments. It can only be administered under strict medical control. Opium and its derivatives are dangerous drugs and their possession by members of the general public is illegal.

Pastinaca sativa L.
Parsnip

VI–VIII
VIII–IX

Umbelliferae

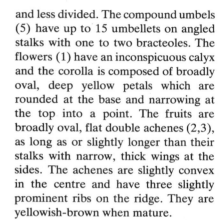

● This is a biennial herb, 40–100 cm (16–39 in) tall, with a beet-like smell. It has a spindle-shaped, light yellow root (4) which is thickened into a beetroot shape in cultivated varieties. In the first year, a rosette of basal leaves grows from the root. These are long-stalked, three to four times pinnate with three to seven pairs of lateral leaflets. The leaflets are lobed, irregularly oval and coarsely toothed. In the second year an erect, angularly furrowed stem, branched in the upper part, grows from the root. The stem leaves are alternate, the lower ones on short stalks, the upper ones sessile with a broadened sheath, and less divided. The compound umbels (5) have up to 15 umbellets on angled stalks with one to two bracteoles. The flowers (1) have an inconspicuous calyx and the corolla is composed of broadly oval, deep yellow petals which are rounded at the base and narrowing at the top into a point. The fruits are broadly oval, flat double achenes (2,3), as long as or slightly longer than their stalks with narrow, thick wings at the sides. The achenes are slightly convex in the centre and have three slightly prominent ribs on the ridge. They are yellowish-brown when mature.

● Wild Parsnip grows in both damp and dry meadows and pastures, on hillsides, in ditches and along riversides. It flowers in July and August. The cultivated varieties with thick roots are used for medicinal purposes.

The achenes germinate within three to four weeks, so they are sown either in late autumn or in very early spring in rows 30 cm (12 in) apart. The seedlings are thinned to a distance of 10–12 cm (4–4 $\frac{3}{4}$ in). It is an undemanding vegetable, does not require watering and will grow even in the semi-shade.

The root has medicinal properties and is also used as a vegetable. It contains vitamins A and C. It has diuretic properties and stimulates the appetite and so is used to treat kidney and gastric problems and constipation. It may be eaten as a vegetable or taken in the form of a decoction. Sweetened with honey, the decoction is used as an anti-tussive in popular medicine. When the fresh roots are not available, the foliage can substitute. Frequent handling of the fresh plant may cause inflamed skin. Home medicines made from Parsnip should be used sparingly, infrequently and in small quantities because it contains constituents which can stimulate the formation of malignant tumours.

Decoction for kidney and gastric problems: simmer two scraped roots in 1 litre (1 $\frac{3}{4}$ pints) milk, sweeten with sugar and take 5 ml (1 teaspoon) every half hour.

IV

 V–VIII

Petasites hybridus
(L.) PR. GÄRTN., B. MEY et SCHERB.

Butterbur
Compositae

● This perennial herb grows to 40–100 cm (16–39 in) in height. It has thick, long, richly branched rhizomes which grow over a considerable area. From these are produced simple flowering stems, which are about 40 cm (16 in) tall in the flowering period and which elongate considerably after the flowers have faded. They are densely covered with sparsely hairy scales which are reddish in colour. At the tip, there is a rich raceme or panicle of flower heads with dingy pink flowers. The plant is dioecious, but in the centre of the flower heads there are several bisexual flowers. Rosettes of basal leaves later grow beside the flower-bearing stems. They are robust, on long stalks and have kidney-shaped or heart-shaped blades which are regularly toothed at the edges. On the upper side, the blade is dark green, with only a few scattered hairs, and on the underside grey and wavy when young, later glabrous and light green. Only the nerves are glandularly hairy on the underside. The fruits are angled, smooth achenes with white to slightly greyish, glossy, simple down at the top.

● Butterbur grows in large patches on lowlands and uplands, in marshes, waterlogged meadows, along the banks of streams and rivers and in wet woods. It flowers from March to May.

Dig up the rhizomes and roots. Rinse them and dry by artificial heat. Sometimes the leaves are collected. Collect these, together with the petioles, until the period when they are attacked by rusts, which occurs in late summer and autumn. The leaves contain a lot of water, so dry them side by side by artificial heat. The dried leaves must not be squashed or become damp and should be stored in well-sealed containers. They must remain green.

Butterbur is used only in popular healing. Antitussive and fever-reducing teas are prepared from it. Teas for treating hoarseness are also made. The rhizome is boiled in wine with honey. For a diuretic preparation, the powder from the dried rhizomes is simmered in a decoction made from rice, semolina or oatflakes. Butterbur has also been used to treat asthma, breathing difficulties and spasms in smooth muscle, as well as externally to treat varicose veins, haemorrhoids and slow-healing wounds.

> **Decoction for coughs and hoarseness:** simmer 10 g ($\frac{2}{3}$ oz) dried rhizome in 500 ml (18 fl oz) wine with honey.

Petroselinum crispum (Miller) Nym. et A. W. Hill
Parsley

VI–VIII

VIII–IX

VIII–X

Umbelliferae

● Parsley is a biennial herb, 30–80 cm (12–31 in) tall, with a vertical, spindle-shaped (in less favourable conditions even branched), yellow-ochre root (4) with numerous fine lateral rootlets. Only the basal leaves grow in the first year. They are long-stalked, triangular in outline, and two to three times pinnately divided into oval or wedge-shaped sections which are un-evenly lobed. They are dark green, glossy and glabrous on the upper side. Varieties cultivated for the foliage have a fuzzy leaf blade and a thin, often branched, root. In the second year erect, richly branched, finely furrowed, hollow stems grow from the root. The upper branches are usually opposite or even arranged in whorls. The stem leaves are alternate, the lower ones being stalked and the upper ones sessile with a broadened sheath. They are simpler than the basal leaves. The upper leaf sections are narrow, tapering and entire. The yellowish-green flowers (1) are arranged in umbels composed of 10–20 umbellets. The envelope is formed of one to three tapering bracts. The fruits are oval achenes (2,3).

● Parsley originates from the Near East and south-eastern Europe. Many varieties are cultivated as a culinary herb. It flowers in June and July.

Sow seeds in late autumn or in very early spring, as it takes several weeks for them to germinate. The plants will survive throughout the winter under snow or under a light cover, so that it is always possible to harvest the fresh leaves. It can also be forced from the roots, if these are planted in pots and left in a warm spot near a window.

The dried haulm is used in popular medicine, but it is not so effective as it is when fresh. The seeds also have medicinal properties.

Parsley relaxes the smooth muscle, so it may have a beneficial effect on urine excretion and on the digestive tract. It must be used with care in home medicines as excessive doses of fresh parsley damage the kidneys and cause mild narcosis in the central nervous system. It irritates the uterine muscle and can cause bleeding outside the menstrual period or increase the flow during it. Bandages may be soaked in the fresh juice and placed on wounds, swellings and insect stings. Parsley medicines should never be taken during pregnancy and large doses should be avoided at all times.

Extract from the Polish pharmacopoeia for kidney and urinary tract inflammation and for digestive disorders, particularly swellings caused by insufficient production of urine: macerate 5 g ($\frac{1}{5}$ oz) seeds in 200 ml (7 fl oz) water and take in two to three doses during the day.

Phaseolus coccineus L.
Kidney Bean

Leguminosae

● This is a perennial in regions not affected by frost. Otherwise, it is an annual twining herb. The stems grow to lengths of up to 4 m (157 in). They twine anti-clockwise and are made rough by scattered hook-like hairs. The leaves are alternate, on long petioles and trimerous. The lateral oval, pointed leaflets have short petioles, the central leaflet having a long petiole. At the petiole there are two short, small bracts. From the leaf axils grow rich racemes of vivid red or white flowers, which are longer than the supporting leaf. The flowers are stalked and grow from the axils of deciduous bracts. They have a two-lipped calyx and a symmetrical corolla consisting of five loose petals, the lower ones of which form a small keel and terminate in a small beak which coils in a spiral. Of the 10 stamens, one is separate and nine fused by the filaments. The ovary is superior and sessile and formed by a single carpel. It matures into large green pods which turn brown while maturing and are rough on the surface. The pericarp is pulpy when young but papery and membranous after maturing. The pods contain black, white or violet and red-spotted, kidney-shaped seeds.

● Kidney Bean is native to tropical America and is widely cultivated in Europe as a vegetable. It flowers from June to September. It requires light, humous soils with a sufficient calcium content. Sow in early May, so that the seeds sprout in the second half of May when there is no danger of night frosts. They are sown close to canes or supports at least 250 cm (98 in) high, 40—50 cm (16—20 in) apart. The immature, soft pods are eaten as a vegetable and are picked from July up to the first frosts. The immature raw seeds contain cyanic compounds and are poisonous. Cases of poisoning have been recorded in children. It is also essential to boil dried kidney beans for 15 minutes to destroy poisonous compounds. The husks of the mature pods, that is the discarded remnants after the harvesting of the mature

seeds, have medicinal properties. They contain substances which lower the blood-sugar level, so they are added to teas used as an auxiliary medicine for mild forms of diabetes. They are also slightly diuretic and are sometimes

blended with other diuretic herbs to make teas to treat bladder and kidney complaints and rheumatism. The powder from the ground seeds may be sprinkled on inflamed skin and itching types of eczema.

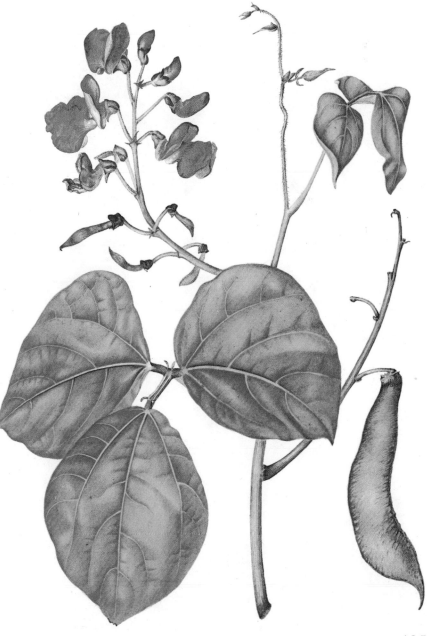

Physalis alkekengi L.
Cape Gooseberry

Solanaceae

● This perennial herb has a creeping, richly branched, slender rhizome (1). There are numerous, erect, 20–60 cm (8–24 in) tall, bluntly angled, simple or slightly branched stems which are downy in the upper part. The leaves are almost oppositely arranged, stalked and oval, either narrowing in a wedge shape towards the petiole or almost notched, entire or with sparse shallow toothing, and pointed. In the leaf axils grow single, rarely two, flowers on short stalks. They have a bell-shaped, sparsely hairy calyx divided into five triangular lobes. During flowering it is a light green with dark green veins and later vermilion red and swollen. The wheel-shaped corolla is a dingy white or greenish, and divided into five broadly pointed, finely downy petals. Among these alternate five stamens with yellow anthers. The superior ovary, which has a style terminating in a club-shaped stigma, matures into a red, glossy berry (2) enclosed in an enlarged red calyx. It contains kidney-shaped seeds.

● Cape Gooseberry grows in deciduous woods, usually oakwoods, hedges, on overgrown rocky slopes or wild along waysides. It is cultivated as an ornamental plant in gardens. It flowers from May to August and is propagated in spring by means of rhizome cuttings.

The mature fruits have medicinal properties. They may be used fresh or dried in the shade in nets. When dried with artificial heat, the temperature should not exceed 40 ° C (104 ° F).

The fruits are rich in vitamin C and are, therefore, recommended for fatigue or during convalescence following infectious illnesses. They stimulate the excretion of uric acid and so are used as a diuretic preparation to treat kidney and urinary tract diseases, and additionally for gout and rheumatism. In popular healing, they were also used to treat liver and gallbladder diseases. The fruits can be preserved by bottling them in syrup or fermenting them in wine. This used to be taken warm in the morning on an empty stomach for kidney stones. A decoction made from the haulm was added to children's baths to soothe skin conditions, rashes and eczema, as well as being used preventively.

Extract for diseases of the urinary tracts and dropsy: macerate 15–30 g (½–1 oz) mature fruits in 500 ml (18 fl oz) water. Take the extract in two doses during the day.

Picea abies (L.) KARSTEN
Norway Spruce

Pinaceae

● This tree, 50—60 m (164—196 ft) in height, has a conical, pointed crown and a trunk up to 150 cm (59 in) in diameter. The bark is brown when young, later reddish-brown and smooth. In old age it changes into a scaly outer bark that peels off and is at first reddish-brown, then greyish-brown. The buds are conical, pointed, and covered with brown scales. The needles are dense, spirally arranged and 10—25 mm ($\frac{2}{5}$—1 in) long. On branches which catch the sun, they are square and rhomboid in cross-section, on branches in the shade more flattened. They are glossy green on all sides, with pointed tips. The main branches grow in whorls. The flowers are unisexual and the plant monoecious. The male flowers are red, with light green scales underneath. The female ones grow at the ends of the current year's twigs and are arranged in oval to cylindrical, green or red cones which are erect when flowering. Later the cones are drooping (2). They have green or red scales, turning brown at maturity with two winged seeds (1).

● Spruce is distributed throughout northern and central Europe, extending in mountainous regions south-east as far as the Balkans. In northern Europe it also grows on lowlands; in central Europe it is native to predominantly mountain positions. It has also been introduced outside the region of its original distribution and is cultivated as an ornamental tree in gardens. It requires dampish soils and quite high atmospheric humidity and is quite resistant to frost. It flowers from April to June, depending on position.

Norway Spruce is widely used in popular healing, mainly externally for baths and inhalation. A decoction made from the young shoots may be taken internally to treat scurvy, and an antitussive syrup may also be prepared from them. In Romania, a decoction made from the young cones is used like this. The cones are scalded with hot water, left to macerate for two hours and then the extract is boiled with sugar. A decoction made from the branches, the needles and, in some cases, even the young cones, may be added to baths for treating physical or nervous exhaustion and to aid convalescence, particularly after infectious illnesses. Norway Spruce baths may also be beneficial in treating heart or back pain (especially that caused by the kidneys), insomnia, gout, rheumatism, nervous attacks, and inflamed skin. Steam containing turpentine vapours may be inhaled to relieve asthma, bronchial catarrh, whooping cough and other inflammatory throat and respiratory ailments. Ointments and plasters may be prepared from the resin to treat cuts, ulcers, swellings and insect stings etc.

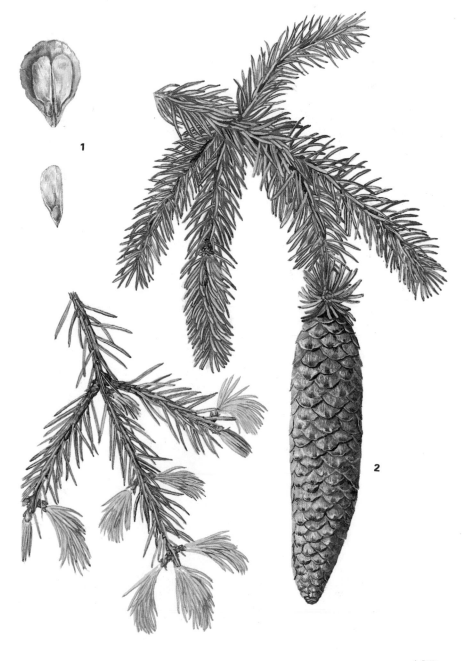

127

Pimpinella saxifraga L.
Burnet Saxifrage

Umbelliferae

● Burnet Saxifrage is a perennial herb which grows to heights of 15—60 cm (6—24 in). It has a spindle-shaped, thick root (3). A rosette of basal leaves grows first. These are odd-pinnate and composed of variously shaped leaflets. They are oval with deep toothing or pinnately divided with both shallow and deep incisions, and sometimes further divided with shallow lobes. Later an erect, rounded stem grows from the rosette of leaves. It is branched in the upper part, finely furrowed and glabrous or with grey down. The stem leaves are alternate and of various shapes. The lower ones are stalked, the central ones sessile with a broadened sheath, both being odd-pinnate, with the leaflets usually deeply pinnate with sections. The upper leaf blades are considerably reduced in size, trifid to simple, composed of linear sections, and attached to the stem by means of a broadened sheath. The stem branches terminate in compound umbels with no bracts. The flowers (1) are very tiny and their petals are coloured white, yellowish or pink. The fruits are short, oval double achenes (2) which are finely ribbed on the outer side.

● Burnet Saxifrage is widespread on dry grasslands, along waysides, in open woodland and on embankments. It flourishes particularly in soils rich in calcium and flowers from July to September.

The roots have medicinal properties. Those of younger plants are harvested in September and October; older ones in March and April. Dig them up, shake off the soil and cut off the aerial parts. Clean, wash quickly and cut lengthwise. Do not immerse them in water for long, as they will become swollen and the essential oils will escape. Dry them in the shade at a temperature of up to 35 ° C (95 ° F). The dried roots can easily become damp or be attacked by insects and should, therefore, be stored in well-sealed containers.

Extracts and decoctions may be prepared with both water and alcohol extracts. These act mainly as anti-tussives for loosening phlegm and as antispasmodics. Burnet Saxifrage also has mild diuretic properties and stimulates the production of gastric juices and bile, and so may be taken to stimulate the appetite. Larger doses cause contractions in the uterine muscle, so it should never be taken during pregnancy. A gargle or mouth rinse is thought to be effective in treating sore throats and gums. A decoction may also be taken for flatulence and rheumatism.

> **Alcohol extract for loss of appetite, gastric problems and flatulence:** macerate 25 g ($\frac{4}{5}$ oz) dried root in 250 ml (9 fl oz) spirit and 250 ml (9 fl oz) water for one week. Take 15 drops on sugar three times daily.

128

Pinus sylvestris L.
Scots Pine

Pinaceae

● This tree, 30—45 m (98—148 ft) in height, has a conical crown when young, later a round loaf-shaped crown, and trunk with a diameter of up to 100 cm (39 in). The smooth bark, which is brown when young, later changes into a thick, greyish-brown outer bark which cracks into plates. The shoots are glabrous and greenish-yellow, the buds reddish-brown and slightly resinous. The branches grow in whorls and the needles in bunches of two. They are greyish-green, tough and curved, with fine spines on the sides which make them rough. On the inner side they have a row of whitish air ducts. When young the needles are enveloped in a thin, papery, greyish membrane. Their skin is greyish-green with a white bloom. They are semi-circular or slightly sickle-shaped in cross-section. They fall in the third year. The flowers are unisexual and the tree monoecious. The male flowers contain small bunches of stamens full of sulphur-yellow pollen and are arranged in oval formations clustered in a spike-like inflorescence at the twig tip. The red female flowers grow individually or in groups of two to three at the branch ends. From them develop greyish-brown, conical cones, which mature after two years.

● Scots Pine grows in sand, on sandy rocks and other rocky slopes, as well as in peat-bogs, thriving both in dry and very wet places. It is widely naturalized outside its natural area of distribution. It flowers mainly in May.

Scots Pine is widely used in popular healing. The pollen contains many medicinal constituents and vitamins.

Alcohol extract for lung complaints, gout and rheumatism: steep 10 g ($\frac{2}{5}$ oz) fresh buds in 100 ml (3 $\frac{1}{2}$ fl oz) spirit and macerate for two days. Filter and take 15—20 drops daily.

Compresses for rheumatic joints: soak 500 g (18 oz) fresh needles in 2 litres (3 $\frac{1}{2}$ pints) water for two hours and simmer for one hour. Wrap the compresses in bandages.

Collect the sprouting buds before they open and dry them in thin layers in the shade in natural heat. The resin and fresh needles are also used in popular healing.

Geriatric medicines for treating disease symptoms in the ageing body are manufactured from the pollen. In popular healing, an alcohol extract is prepared from the sprouting buds. The more elongated young shoots are placed in a saturated sugar solution and left for several weeks. The solution is then taken in spoonfuls for coughs, hoarseness and sore throats. Baths may also be prepared from them for treating gout and rheumatism: boil 1 kg (2 lb 3 oz) shoots in 3 litres (5 $\frac{1}{4}$ pints) water for $\frac{1}{2}$ hour and add to the bath. The older needles may also be used for this. The warmed resin spread on cloth is used for hot compresses on rheumatic areas.

129

Plantago lanceolata L.
Ribwort Plantain

V–IX

Plantaginaceae

● Ribwort Plantain is a low-growing perennial herb with a short, vertical rhizome. A rosette of basal leaves grows from it. They are tapering, with parallel veins, and gradually narrowed towards the base, entire or with inconspicuous, widely spaced teeth, pointed, mainly erect, and predominantly with five main, short, white hairy nerves. From the axils of the basal leaves grow leafless stems up to 50 cm (20 in) high, which are either erect or short and ascending, have five lengthwise furrows and are covered with short, erect white hairs. They terminate in a spike of flowers which is conical when young. Later it elongates into a cylindrical shape, reaching lengths of around 4 cm ($1\frac{1}{2}$ in). The flowers grow in the axils of brown, dry membranous bracts. The calyx is composed of two loose and two fused sepals which are erect, oval, pointed and transparent with a green central nerve. The corolla is a tubular funnel shape, divided into four brownish-pink tips narrowing into an oval and opening out into a bowl shape. Protruding from the corolla on long filaments are four stamens with yellow anthers. The fruit is an oval capsule.

● Ribwort Plantain grows abundantly in meadows and pastures, along field paths, in ditches, gardens, open woodland, in fields as a weed, on dumping grounds, road and railway embankments and other waste places. It flowers from May to September.

Collect the foliage during the flowering period from non-polluted locations. It is cultivated for the pharmaceutical industry. Sow the seeds in March in rows 30–40 cm (12–16 in) apart, 2–3 cm ($\frac{3}{4}$–1 in) deep. Leaves from plants fertilized with potassium have up to twice the amount of active constituents; otherwise the plant does not require any other fertilizer or special care. Cut the leaves from flowering plants only and dry them in thin layers, without turning, in the shade at a temperature of up to 40 °C (104 °F). They must not turn black or brown and should not be squashed together in storage containers.

Anti-tussive syrups and medicinal expectorant teas are prepared by the pharmaceutical industry. Ribwort Plantain also contains constituents which stimulate digestion and the appetite. A decoction may be used on compresses on slow-healing wounds, as it has disinfectant properties. It also softens hard skin. A decoction is suitable as a gargle or mouth rinse. The fresh juice relieves bee stings.

Extract for ailments of the respiratory organs associated with heavy phlegm: macerate 5 g ($\frac{1}{5}$ oz) dry, chopped leaves in 200 ml (7 fl oz) boiling water for about 15 minutes.

130

Plantago media L.
Lamb's Tongue Plantain

Plantaginaceae

● This perennial plant has a long, spindle-shaped, brown, often many-headed root which penetrates the soil at an angle. On its top grow rosettes of broadly oval basal leaves. They have five to nine small veins which are parallel at the tips, and narrow at the base in a wedge shape towards the broad, short petiole. They are either entire or sparsely toothed, covered with scattered hair, and for the most part appressed to the ground. From their axils grow short, ascending, leafless stalks, rounded in cross-section, covered with curly pubescent hair in the upper part and terminating in a cylindrical spike of flowers. The flowers grow in the axils of oval pointed bracts which have white borders and are downy. The glabrous calyx is composed of four oval sepals. The whitish corolla is divided into four flatly opened lobes, from which protrude pink to violet filaments with yellow anthers. The pistil has a globular green ovary with a red, filamentous style. The fruit is an oval capsule pointed at the tip and opening in the centre through a lid.

● This plant grows on lowlands and uplands in dry meadows and pastures, in open woodland and hedgerows and on rocky slopes.

Collect the leaves from May to September in the flowering period and dry them in thin layers in the shade without turning. In some places, the medicinal properties of Lamb's Tongue Plantain are thought to be the same as those of Ribwort Plantain, although it has a somewhat different content of active constituents, for example, fewer mucilages. In fact, Lamb's Tongue Plantain

may even be given precedence over Ribwort Plantain in popular healing, for several reasons. Lamb's Tongue Plantain grows in habitats far less threatened by pollution, its leaves are less prone to turning black during drying, and the flowering spikes of Lamb's Tongue Plantain are more attractive in appearance. Apart from this, it also has a pleasant smell, so that some herbalists believe that it is, therefore, more effective (in many plants the presence of certain active constituents really does manifest itself in the smell).

It is not only used as an anti-tussive, but also for gastric problems, liver complaints, enlarged spleen and for headaches of nervous origin. Apart from normal tea, a decoction in milk may also be prepared, as well as an extract in white wine or pure spirit and syrup.

> **Syrup made from spirit extract for irritating coughs:** macerate 30 g (1 oz) partly dried leaves in 25 ml (1 fl oz) spirit. When the spirit has soaked into the leaves, add 200 ml (8 fl oz) boiling water. Macerate for 24 hours, mixing occasionally, strain, and boil with 300 g (10 $\frac{1}{2}$ oz) sugar. Take one teaspoonful morning and evening.

Polygonum aviculare L.
Knotgrass

Polygonaceae

● Knotgrass is an annual herb the stem of which grows to heights of up to 15 cm (6 in). The root is spindle-shaped, slender, and branched. From it grow numerous round, furrowed, angled, slender and richly leafed stems which are branched from the very bottom and which form either a thick growth appressed to the ground or small shrub-like, ascending, sparse tufts. The leaves are alternate and either without stalks or on short stalks, oval to tapering, usually pointed, entire and glabrous or with fine bristles at the edges, close to the stem with a dry membranous, paper-like bract frayed at the ends. The tiny flowers (3) grow in groups of two to five in the leaf axils. They have a white, greenish or pinkish perianth consisting of five triangular petals which terminate at the base in a funnel shape. They contain eight stamens which are much shorter than the petals, the stamen filaments broadening at the base. The pistil has a superior ovary consisting of three carpels with three short styles. The fruit is a three-sided, blackish-brown achene (1) which is pointed at the tip and enclosed in a desiccated, brownish perianth (2).

● Knotgrass grows in masses in fields, along waysides and other well-trodden places, on dumping grounds, bare ground, paths and embankments. It thrives in both completely dry and damper places on lowlands and uplands.

Collect the flowering haulm throughout the summer until autumn. Pull up the whole plant, including the roots. Cut off the stems. Wash the haulm and dry it in the shade at a temperature of up to 45 °C (113 °F) in thin layers. Do not turn it, otherwise the leaflets and flowers will fall off. Collect the plants from places which are not dusty, where they do not suffer from pollution and harmful substances from the environment.

Knotgrass has diuretic properties and facilitates the excretion of unwanted substances. It is also haemostatic and is said to have beneficial effects on diabetes. It stimulates digestion and body metabolism. It may be taken to treat diseases of the urinary tract, kidney stones, rheumatism, gout, gastric and digestive problems, loss of appetite, diarrhoea and chronic bronchitis. It usually forms part of tea blends with other herbs having comparable properties. It may be applied to inflamed skin and used for bathing inflamed abscesses, for compresses, and for rinsing the mouth and gargling.

> **Extract for diseases of the urinary tract and for kidney stones:** scald 10–15 ml (2–3 teaspoons) dried haulm in 500 ml (18 fl oz) boiling water. Take the extract during the day.

132

Polygonum bistorta L.
Common Bistort

Polygonaceae

This perennial herb grows up to 100 cm (39 in) tall. The rhizome is pulpy and cylindrical, with brown skin, almost white or pinkish inside, and penetrated with black vascular bundles and covered with fine roots. At the top grows a rosette of basal leaves and usually a single stem. The basal leaves are oval or tapering, either entire or finely furrowed and bristly at the edges. They are dark green on the upper side and greyish green on the underside, with long winged petioles. The stem leaves are alternate, on short petioles or almost without stalks and with heart-shaped indentations. At the tip of the stem, there is a single, spike-like, contracted, cylindrical cluster of light pink, rarely white, flowers. The flowers have five oval erect petals. Protruding from the perianth there are five to eight stamens on long filaments with dark red small glands at the base and reddish-violet anthers. The pistil has three styles at the tip. The fruit is a three-sided, glossy brown achene, pointed at the top and enclosed in the desiccated perianth.

Common Bistort grows in damp to peaty meadows, along the banks of streams, at spring sources, and typically in hay meadows. It grows on lowlands and uplands and is commonest in the Pennines. It flowers in July and August.

Dig up the rhizomes in spring or autumn. Remove the smaller surface roots, wash the rhizomes and cut them up into several smaller pieces. Dry them in the shade at a temperature of up to 40 ° C (104 ° F). Store in well-sealed containers. The haulm is also used in popular healing. Cut it off from May to August and dry in the shade in natural heat.

A decoction or tea made from the root is used both internally and externally as a haemostatic. It also has anti-inflammatory properties, as it checks the reproduction of bacteria, and is effective against diarrhoea. It is also recommended for treating ulcers in the digestive tract, diarrhoea with blood in the stool and other digestive disorders, such as dysentery, when it helps to reduce the need for antibiotics. A decoction may be used as a mouth rinse for bleeding and inflammatory gums and as a gargle for sore throat. It may be put on compresses to treat slow-healing wounds und ulcers, scalds and leg abscesses. The haulm is rich in silicic acid. A decoction is effective in dissolving kidney stones formed of calcium oxalate.

Tea for treating diarrhoea: boil 25 g ($\frac{4}{5}$ oz) dried rhizome in 500 ml (18 fl oz) water for 10 minutes. Take in several doses during the day.

Polypodium vulgare L.
Polypody

Polypodiaceae

● Polypody is a perennial fern. The creeping rhizome, which is up to 40 cm (16 in) long, grows either slightly buried in the soil or along its surface, in moss, on rocks, roots, rotting wood or humous soil. It is either simple or only slightly branched, sweetish and pungent to the taste and densely covered with tapering brown glumes. The leaves grow from it sparsely in two rows, generally surviving the winter. They are up to 40 cm (16 in) long and triangular to tapering, the blade usually being longer than the petiole and pinnately divided into alternate, tapering or even oval, blunt, finely toothed sections which have no stems. There are up to 25 pairs of these. The small lateral veins branch out fork-like several times. There are two rows of round clusters of spore cases (1) at the ends of these between the central small vein and the edge of the section. The whole plant is glabrous. The spores (2) mature from August to September and the sporangia (3) are a golden rusty colour.

● Polypody grows mainly on damp rocks or mossy boulders, in woods, sometimes even on rotting wood, bare roots, stumps or on stony or gravelly soil. It also grows on old walls and, in a sufficiently moist atmosphere, even as an epiphyte on the moss-overgrown bark of old trees. It grows on lowlands and uplands, but is scarce in eastern Britain. It is also cultivated in gardens on rockeries or walls. It requires humous soil with a sand and peat admixture. It is propagated by division of the rhizomes.

Collect the rhizomes in spring or autumn. Remove the small roots, leaves and petiole remnants, wash the rhizomes with water and dry either in natural or artificial heat. The rhizome is crumbly after being dried, greenish at the break and retains its sweet taste. It may not be stored for more than a year, as it loses its efficacy with time.

A decoction or extract made with boiling water as an anti-tussive facilitates the loosening of phlegm. It also has laxative and diuretic properties and is, therefore, recommended for bladder inflammation. In popular healing, Polypody is also used for treating parasitic worms and for improving gall production.

Anti-tussive decoction or for treating bladder inflammation: boil 20 g ($\frac{3}{4}$ oz) dried rhizome in 250 ml (9 fl oz) water for five minutes and filter immediately. Take 30 ml (1 tablespoon) three times daily.

buds II—IV

III—IV

V—VI

Populus tremula L.
Aspen

Salicaceae

This tree grows to heights of 25—30 m (82—98 ft). It has smooth, greenish-grey bark which, when old, changes in the lower part into a black, fissured outer bark. The annual shoots are slender and a glossy yellowish-brown or brown. The older twigs are ash grey to blackish grey. The buds are alternate, conical and sharply pointed, light to dark brown and glossy, being covered with scales. On the lateral twigs grow thicker, ovate-globose flower buds. The leaves are alternate, oval or triangular to rhomboid, notched at the base and larger (on the young shoots), with silky hair when young, later glabrous, and coarsely and irregularly toothed, with a flattened petiole. The plant is dioecious. The unisexual flowers are arranged in drooping catkins, of which the supporting bracts (1) are dark brown, deeply lobed and covered with dense, long grey hair. There are 4—12 stamens with carmine-red anthers (2). The ovaries (3) are conical with four purplish-red, erect stigmas (4).

This tree grows predominantly in damp woods and on moors on lowlands and uplands. It flowers in March, the seeds in the capsules maturing in May. It propagates by means of seeds, which are easily borne away on the wind as they are equipped with fine down. They rapidly lose their ability to germinate. Sow them in frames or directly into the ground immediately after maturing. Propagate vegetatively by means of root off-shoots or root cuttings. Aspen requires plenty of light.

Collect the buds before they sprout. Dry them slowly and store in well-sealed containers. Peel the bark from the thin branches at the beginning of spring when sap is flowing in them. Dry as quickly as possible at a temperature of around 60 ° C (140 ° F). The leaves also have medicinal properties. Dry them quickly so that they do not turn black.

The buds have considerable diuretic and anti-bacterial properties. An extract made with boiling water may be taken internally for inflammation of the urinary tract, enlarged prostate problems, and for gout and rheumatism. An ointment prepared from the fresh buds may be applied externally to ease rheumatic pain and burns. The buds are also used in cosmetic preparations. An extract made from the bark with boiling water may be taken for diarrhoea, excessive menstrual bleeding and for treating parasitic worms. It can be applied on compresses to inflamed skin and ulcers. The leaves are used for the same purpose as the bark. An extract made with boiling water may also be taken internally to treat rheumatism.

Extract for rheumatism and parasitic worms: pour 1 litre (1 ¾ pints) boiling water over 90 ml (3 tablespoons) crushed dried leaves and leave to macerate for 10 minutes. Take in doses of 200 ml (7 fl oz) twice daily.

135

Potentilla anserina L.
Silverweed

 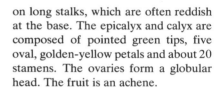
Rosaceae

This is a low, perennial herb with a thick, short, sometimes even corm-like, branched rhizome with an abundance of long, brown rootlets. A rich rosette of basal leaves and numerous creeping, up to 1 m (39 in) long rooting stems grow from the rhizome. The leaves are odd-pinnate, up to 20 cm (8 in) long, elongated in contour, somewhat broader in the upper part, glabrous or with silvery hair on the upper side and with silky white felt on the underside. The individual leaflets are elongated to oval, without stalks, and deeply toothed to almost pinnately lobed. The stipules are large and brown with darker small veins and pointed. The cylindrical, reddish stems take root at the places where they swell, forming further leaves and flowers. The flowers grow individually on long stalks, which are often reddish at the base. The epicalyx and calyx are composed of pointed green tips, five oval, golden-yellow petals and about 20 stamens. The ovaries form a globular head. The fruit is an achene.

Silverweed grows on commons, along waysides, the banks of ponds, streams and rivers, in bogs, reed beds, ditches, gravelly and sandy deposits, around villages and towns and in geese-runs. Geese do not eat Silverweed, but feed on surrounding plants, thus ridding it of competition. The goose manure richly supports its growth. It is distributed on lowlands and uplands and flowers from May to August.

The leaves and rhizomes have medicinal properties. Collect the foliage during the flowering period and dry it spread out in thin layers. Dig up the rhizomes in spring or autumn. Wash them thoroughly and dry slowly by artificial heat in the shade.

A decoction or spirit extract of the rhizome is used both internally and externally. It acts mainly on smooth muscle, but also on the gall duct and stimulates the formation of gastric juices, and intestinal peristalsis. It helps to check internal bleeding. It is recommended in blends with other medicinal plants, for uterine, intestinal and gallbladder spasms, menstrual pain caused by spasms, flatulence, chronic gastric ulcers and for ulcers in other parts of the digestive system, as well as for diarrhoea. The fresh leaves may be placed on wounds, contusions and inflamed skin.

Decoction for diarrhoea: simmer 20 g ($\frac{3}{4}$ oz) dried rhizome in 250 ml (9 fl oz) water for three minutes. Take 30 ml (2 tablespoons) three times daily.

Spirit extract for biliousness: macerate 20 g ($\frac{3}{4}$ oz) dried rhizome in 100 ml (3 $\frac{1}{2}$ fl oz) spirit for five days. Take 10 drops in a spoonful of water before meals four times daily.

Potentilla erecta (L.) Raeusch
Tormentil

Rosaceae

● Tormentil is a perennial herb 20–40 cm (8–16 in) tall. The rhizome, which penetrates the soil at an angle, is spindle-shaped to corm-like and swollen, often multi-headed (1), with a tendency to turn woody, reddish-brown to blackish-brown, salmon red in cross-section and having five bands of vascular bundles arranged in a star shape. Numerous small fibre-like rootlets grow on the rhizome. Rosettes of basal leaves on long stalks grow from it. These are palmately divided into three to five segments. The individual leaflets are oval, narrowing in a wedge shape towards the petiole, coarsely toothed and entire in the lower part. The erect, ascending or even procumbent stems do not take root. They have scattered, appressed hair and are densely leafy, being sparsely branched in the upper half. The stem leaves are mostly without stalks and arranged in threes, the uppermost ones undivided, glabrous or softly downy. The tiny flowers grow individually on long stalks from the leaf axils. The epicalyx and calyx are composed of four sepals and the golden-yellow corolla consists of four heart-shaped petals. The fruits are oval achenes.

● Tormentil grows in both damp and dry grasslands, in forests, marshes, heaths, sandy places and clearings on lowlands and uplands. It flowers from May to September.

Pull up the rhizomes carefully in spring or in autumn after the flowers have faded. Remove the aerial parts and dry remnants, clean, and rinse quickly so that the rhizomes do not absorb water. Dry as quickly as possible at a temperature of up to 40 ° C (104 ° F). Store in well-sealed containers.

Tormentil is recommended for diarrhoea, bleeding, and as an anti-inflammatory preparation which checks the reproduction of bacteria. It may also be taken for chronic and acute inflammation of the digestive system and gastric ulcers and used as a gargle or mouth rinse to treat inflamed gums. It may be applied externally on spots and boils and in compresses on slow-healing wounds. The daily dose for diarrhoea is 0.5–3 g ($1\frac{1}{50}-\frac{1}{10}$ oz). An extract for internal use is prepared from 10 g ($\frac{2}{3}$ oz) dried rhizome in 300 ml ($10\frac{1}{2}$ fl oz) water. Take 5–10 ml (1–2 teaspoons) several times daily. For external use on compresses, macerate 15–20 g ($\frac{1}{2}-\frac{3}{4}$ oz) dried rhizome in 200 ml (7 fl oz) water. The extract is used for bathing suppurating boils and for cleansing the skin. Compresses for the night may also be prepared from it.

1

Spirit extract for diarrhoea: macerate 20 g ($\frac{3}{4}$ oz) chopped dried rhizome in 100 ml ($3\frac{1}{2}$ fl oz) pure spirit and take 10 drops in a spoonful of water before meals four times daily.

137

Primula elatior (L.) Hill
Oxlip

Primulaceae

● This perennial herb grows to 30 cm (12 in) in height. It has a cylindrical, somewhat crooked rhizome. A rosette of basal leaves grows from it. These are inrolled at the edges when young, wrinkled, oval and round at the tip. They narrow abruptly towards the base into a broad, winged stalk. The blade is greyish-green on the underside, irregularly crenate to toothed and pointed, and hairy. The cylindrical, leafless stalk bears an umbel of flowers with an envelope composed of tapering bracteoles. The flowers grow on stalks and are usually bent down to one side. They have a narrow, cylindrical calyx with prominent edges and are joined to the corolla tube. They are divided into five teeth at the top. The sulphur-yellow, regular corolla, the tube of which protrudes only slightly from the calyx, is divided into five flatly spreading, heart-shaped petals. The corolla tube contains five stamens with yellow anthers and a pistil with a club-shaped stigma. The fruit is a cylindrical capsule which opens by means of a toothed mouth.

● Oxlip grows in damp, sufficiently nutritious soils. In Britain, it is only found in Essex. It flowers from March to May, depending on the position.

Dig up the rhizome, together with the roots, either during the flowering period or in autumn and at the beginning of winter, when the active constituent content reaches a second peak. Clean thoroughly, wash quickly in water and dry at a temperature of up to 40 °C (104 °F). The plant is a protected species in many countries and would be seriously threatened by the collection of the underground parts, so collect only from cultivated plants. The inflorescence of the related species, the Cowslip (*Primula veris*) (1), has medicinal properties. Cowslip is widespread in drier places.

Oxlip can be cultivated by direct sowing into loose, moist and nutritious soil. To obtain the seeds, pick the dry stalks together with the capsules once they have turned brown and contain the mature seeds in June or July. Sow in a cold frame and later prick out the seedlings.

A decoction made from the rhizome may be taken to improve expectoration, particularly in cases of a dry cough, inflammation of the upper respiratory passages, bronchitis, inflammation of the throat, and gout. Oxlip must be used as a home medicine with care and restraint, as excessive doses irritate the digestive system and can cause vomiting. It is very often combined with Coltsfoot leaves, Lavender flowers and Hops.

1

Decoction for gout: boil 15 g ($\frac{1}{2}$ oz) dried rhizome in 250 ml (9 fl oz) water. Take 1 teaspoon daily.

Prunus avium (L.) MOENCH
Wild Cherry

Rosaceae

● This tree, up to 20 m (66 ft) in height, has an oval crown and reddish-brown bark when young, later greyish-brown to black. The annual shoots are thick and reddish-brown with a grey coating, the lateral twigs short and blackish-brown. The alternate, conical, pointed buds and the short and oval flower buds are covered with reddish-brown scales. The leaves are alternate, oval, pointed at the ends and have toothed edges. The leaf stalk is green, with one or two globular small red glands. The hermaphrodite flowers grow in small bunches. The five calyx lobes have an entire margin and are bent backwards. There are five white oval petals. The lower part of the flower is joined to form a cupule from which grow 20—30 stamens with yellow anthers. Situated inside the cupule is the superior ovary with a furrowed style and an indented stigma. The ovary matures into a globular red drupe. The drupes grow in groups of one to three on long stalks.

● Wild Cherry is distributed throughout almost the whole of Europe, except the northern countries. It is a widespread woodland and hedgerow tree. It is more abundant in valleys and at the foot of slopes, where there is fresh, fertile soil. Several varieties are cultivated as a fruit tree and the double-flowered form is grown as an ornamental tree. It flowers in May. The fruits mature in the second half of June or more frequently in July.

Collect the fruit stalks and dry in moderate heat so that they remain green. They have diuretic properties and are used in popular healing to treat coughs. A bronchial syrup may be prepared from the ripe fruits. The seeds were once also used in popular healing but they are poisonous and should never be used nowadays. Resin from the bark was also once collected and used, diluted with vinegar, to treat skin rashes. It forms part of the mixture of resinous substances collected by bees and used to seal the cracks in their hives. This, known as propolis, is currently being researched. A decoction made from dry cherry leaves may be taken as a substitute for tea.

Prunus spinosa L.
Blackthorn

Rosaceae

III–IV
V
VI
IX–X

This is a shrub or small tree, 1–5 m (3–16 ft) in height. It is thorny and often forms extensive thickets spreading by means of root runners. The shoots are brown with fine grey felt. The older twigs are dark grey, the lateral ones being transformed into thorns. The buds are alternate, tiny and oval, the flower buds are globular and covered with light brown scales. The leaf buds are in groups of two to three, the fower buds being clustered on the short twigs. The leaves are alternate, oval, toothed and hairy. The leaf stalks have no glands. The regular, bisexual flowers open in small bunches before the leaves have sprouted. The calyx is tapering and entire, the petals are pure white, short and oval. The short flower stalks are glabrous. There is a large number of stamens with long filaments and oval, yellow anthers. The superior ovary is deep inside the calyx. It matures into globular or slightly oval drupes with bluish-black skin with a grey bloom.

Blackthorn grows on dry slopes and rocks, at the edges of woods, in scrub, along waysides, on road embankments, in river valleys and in hedges on warm lowlands and uplands. It flowers in March and April.

Collect the flowers shortly after they have opened. You can pick them individually, shake them off on to big sheets, or cut off the richly blossoming twigs whole and pull off the flowers. Always collect them in dry weather and place them loosely in a basket so that they do not become squashed. Dry spread out in thin layers as quickly as possible in the shade at a temperature of up to 40 ° C (104 ° F). Store in well-sealed tins. Peel the bark off the young shoots in May and dry at normal temperatures. Collect the leaves in June, when they have the highest levels of active constituents, and dry in the shade at normal temperatures. Collect the fruits for drying in September or October before they over-ripen, but for preserving or wine only after the first frosts, when they have lost some of their tartness. Dry them without the stalks until they harden and discard any which have turned soft or brown.

An extract made from the flowers has mild diuretic and laxative properties. A decoction made from the bark may be used as a gargle. A decoction made from the leaves with lemon juice may be taken for chills. A spirit extract can be prepared from the dried fruits to treat diarrhoea.

Spirit extract for treating diarrhoea: steep 25 g ($\frac{4}{5}$ oz) dried fruits in 125 ml (4 $\frac{1}{2}$ fl oz) spirit for three days. Take 5 ml (1 teaspoon) twice daily.

Decoction for gargling: boil 20 g ($\frac{3}{4}$ oz) dried bark in 500 ml (18 fl oz) water for 20 minutes.

Pulmonaria officinalis L.
Lungwort

Boraginaceae

● Lungwort is a perennial herb 15–30 cm (6–12 in) in height. The rhizome either penetrates the soil at an angle or is almost horizontal. It is branched, cylindrical, blackish-brown, with numerous perpendicular rootlets. A rosette of basal leaves grows from it. These are long-stalked, heart-shaped or a tapering oval in shape, entire or finely toothed. The stems are of two types: flower-bearing, or leafy and sterile. The oval entire stem leaves are smaller, alternate and sessile, tapering downwards along the stem. The stem terminates in monochasia of flowers. The flowers have a tubular calyx divided into five teeth and a funnel-shaped corolla terminating in five round lobes. The corolla is pink at first, then red and violet, changing into a blue colour when it starts to fade. Rarely it is permanently white. At the mouth of the corolla trumpet there is a tuft of hairs. The filaments of the five stamens have grey anthers. The ovary is superior and the style terminates in a club-shaped stigma. It matures into four oval and pointed nutlets which are smooth on the surface and dark brown to almost black in colour.

● Lungwort grows in open deciduous woodland in humus-rich soils, or in hedgerows, flourishing mainly in damp places on lowlands and uplands. It flowers in April and May.

It can be cultivated in semi-shade or even in shaded places, such as under Hazel trees, in places where there is sufficient humus and the soil is rich in calcium. It is either propagated from seeds, which are sown immediately after maturing in the summer and in autumn, or by the division of older clumps. The young plants are planted 20 cm (8 in) apart in rows 30 cm (12 in) apart.

Collect the haulm during the flowering period or shortly after the flowers have faded. Cut it off close to the ground and place loosely in a basket so that it does not become squashed. Pulling up the plants would damage the perennial rhizomes and pollute the active constituents. Dry as quickly as possible in thin layers or hanging in small bundles at a temperature of up to 40 °C (104 °F). Turn gently during the drying process, but do not damage or squash them, as they would then lose their colour, which can only be retained by rapid drying. The dried haulms easily become damp again, and should therefore be stored in well-sealed containers.

A decoction or extract made with boiling water may be taken internally for coughs, bronchitis, lung complaints and menstrual problems. The decoction is also anti-inflammatory.

Decoction for coughs and hoarseness: boil 40 g (1 $\frac{2}{5}$ oz) in 1 litre (1 $\frac{3}{4}$ pints) water for three minutes. Take 250 ml (9 fl oz) daily, sweetened with honey.

141

Quercus robur L.
Pedunculate Oak

Fagaceae

● This robust tree grows to a height of 30—35 m (98—115 ft). For about the first 20—25 years, the bark is smooth and grey, later cracking lengthwise into a blackish-grey outer bark. The shoots are thick with lengthwise furrowing, olive-green and reddish-brown. The older twigs are ash-grey or greyish-brown. The alternate, broadly oval, roundish, light brown buds are clustered at the ends of the twigs with a larger bud at the tip. The stalked leaves are alternate, oval and shallowly lobed. The blade is indented with lobes at the petiole. The flowers are unisexual, the plant monoecious. The male flowers hang in drooping, interrupted, greenish-yellow catkins, which grow from the leaf axils of the previous year's twigs. The perianth consists of six small felty scales, behind which there are six stamens. The female flowers are situated in the leaf axils of the annual shoots. A round small cup and a six-pointed perianth with a pistil and with a three- to four-lobed red stigma lie behind a supporting bract in four bracteoles.

● Pedunculate Oak is distributed from western Europe to the Urals and grows as far north as Sweden. It grows mainly on heavy lowland soils. It flowers in May simultaneously with the sprouting of the leaves. The fruits are acorns growing in groups of one to three on long stalks and maturing in September and October.

It is cultivated from the acorns, which are sown 4—6 cm ($1\frac{1}{2}$—$2\frac{1}{4}$ in) deep either directly into the ground or in nurseries. The one-year-old saplings, which produce a long taproot, are then replanted.

Collect the bark from younger trunks or from the branches of felled trees in March and April. Make circular incisions 20—30 cm (8—12 in) apart, on the trunk or branches and join them with a lengthwise cut. Tap the bark lightly with a blunt object and peel it off. Dry it in the sun at first, and complete the drying process in drying sheds. Store in well-sealed containers.

A haemostatic decoction is taken internally for treating the digestive tract and for diarrhoea. It is also effective against bacteria, and acts as an antidote in cases of poisoning, for example after overdoses of some medicines or in case of poisoning caused by alkaloids or heavy metals. However, poisoning always requires immediate medical attention and you should not attempt to treat it yourself with home medicines. Pedunculate Oak may also be used on compresses to relieve minor burns and frostbite and to bathe inflammation of the veins, leg abscesses, eczema, inflamed skin, bleeding haemorrhoids and ulcers. It may be used as a mouth wash for treating inflamed gums.

Rhamnus catharticus L.
Buckthorn

Rhamnaceae

● This usually thorny shrub or small tree grows to heights of 3–8 m (10–26 ft). The bark is smooth when young and almost black; later it changes into a papery outer bark which peels off in rolling plates. The grey annual shoots usually terminate in thorns. The buds (1) are arranged in slanting opposite pairs. They are spindle-shaped, pointed and covered with blackish-brown scales which are hairy at the edges. The leaves are oppositely arranged, oval to round, finely toothed with two to four pairs of parallel nerves. The heterosexual flowers grow in small, dense axillary bundles. The calyx is fused at the base and divided into four triangular lobes. The four horizontally open, tapering, greenish petals of the corolla reach twice the length of the calyx. The male flowers have four stamens and the female ones a superior ovary with a long style and a four-part stigma. The fruits, growing either individually or in sparse bunches, are globular drupes which are green when young and glossy black later with green to blackish-violet, sticky pulp. They contain four three-sided, fused pips.

● Buckthorn grows on dry slopes, rocky and stony hillsides and in woodland. It is widespread in lowland England. As it tolerates pruning well, it is suitable for hedges. It grows well in semi-shade and is resistant to frost and drought.

Propagate either from seed or from root cuttings. The seeds are obtained from the ripe, crushed berries. Rinse out the pips and soak them in water for 24 hours to remove the remnants of pulp which slows down germination. Sow in autumn, the seeds germinating only in spring. They usually need to be exposed to frost in order to germinate.

Collect the bark from the young twigs in spring. Make two circular incisions in the bark around the twig at a distance of 10–30 cm (4–12 in). Join with a lengthwise cut, tap with a blunt object and peel off. Dry at a temperature of up to 40 °C (104 °F). The bark has mild laxative properties, although considerably weaker than those of the related Alder Buckthorn. The ripe fruits are mainly used for medicinal purposes. Collect them in September and October. Clean and pick them over, then dry in thin layers at a temperature of 40 °C (104 °F). Store in well-sealed containers. The fruit may be used as a laxative in various preparations, either as a decoction, extract, thickened juice, syrup or preserve. It also stimulates the production of bile.

1

For **persistent constipation** 3–5 g ($\frac{1}{10}$–$\frac{1}{5}$ oz) dried fruits crumbled into honey or plum jam may be taken. For older people, a decoction made from 10 g ($\frac{2}{5}$ oz) fruits in 200 ml (7 fl oz) water is recommended.

Rhamnus frangula (L.) Miller
(syn. *Frangula alnus* L.)

Alder Buckthorn

Rhamnaceae

 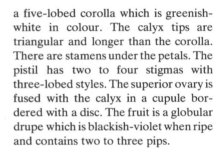

● This shrub or small tree is 3–7 m (10–23 ft) in height. When young it has smooth, violet-brown bark with whitish lenticels or aeration pores, later being greyish-brown, and black when old. The annual shoots are erect, greyish-brown and often rusty and felty towards the tip, with dense whitish lenticels. The buds are alternate, naked and formed of rusty-felted leaflets arranged in folds. The entire leaves are alternate and broadly oval with short points. They have seven to ten pairs of lateral nerves. On the underside the nerves and stalk are hairy, otherwise the blade is glabrous. The bisexual flowers grow on stalks in the leaf axils in small bunches of two to ten. They have a joined calyx and a five-lobed corolla which is greenish-white in colour. The calyx tips are triangular and longer than the corolla. There are stamens under the petals. The pistil has two to four stigmas with three-lobed styles. The superior ovary is fused with the calyx in a cupule bordered with a disc. The fruit is a globular drupe which is blackish-violet when ripe and contains two to three pips.

● Alder Buckthorn grows over large areas of Europe, even far to the north, in damp to marshy places, in alder groves, woodland, acid oak groves, damp pinewoods and sometimes even on rocks. It flowers from June to August. In late summer there are both flowers and ripe and unripe fruits on the shrubs at the same time. Alder Buckthorn can be cultivated both from woody cuttings and from seeds, which are exposed to frost during the winter and sown in spring either into frames or directly into the ground.

Collect the bark from the young branches from March to May. Make two circular cuts 10–30 cm (4–12 in) apart on young branches. Join them with a lengthwise cut, tap with a blunt instrument and peel off. Cut off and burn the shoots from which the bark has been removed. The shrubs regenerate well. Dry the bark in the sun or by artificial heat at a temperature of up to 40 °C (104 °F). While drying, it rolls up. Store in bags in a dry place. Do not use the dried bark for one year or first heat it to 100 °C (212 °F) for one hour. Otherwise it has an unpleasant smell and causes vomiting.

Extracts or a decoction may be taken internally as a laxative and to destroy parasitic worms and some protozoa. Alder Buckthorn is widely used in Siberia for treating liver and gallbladder disorders, dropsy, chills and intestinal parasites. It is used externally for treating scabies. In popular healing, the dried ripe fruits or preserves made from the fruits are used as a laxative. Take 5 ml (1 teaspoon) dried fruits or preserve once only.

Rheum officinale L.
Medicinal Rhubarb

Polygonaceae

● Medicinal or Turkey Rhubarb is a stout perennial herb, the stems of which grow to heights of 2.5−3 m (8−10 ft). In the first year, the seedlings produce a thick, spindle-shaped root. Subsequently this becomes a robust multi-headed rhizome with long, thick roots. It is yellow inside and covered on the surface with a brownish-yellow barky layer. Robust basal leaves grow from it. They have long, thick stalks and round to kidney-shaped blades, which are shallowly indented from the edges into five unevenly shaped lobes. Both the stalks and the leaf blades are glabrous and the stalk with its main nerves is sometimes reddish in colour. The erect, thick, hollow stems, which are branched in the upper part, have several alternate leaves and terminate in rich and dense panicles of tiny flowers. The calyx is divided into six lobes, the corolla being formed of six white, yellowish or pinkish petals in groups of three and arranged in two circles in groups of six plus three. The superior, three-sided ovary has three stigmas terminating in globular styles. The inflorescence elongates substantially after fading, maturing into achenes with a winged pericarp.

● It originates from central Asia but a number of cultivars, including hybrids with other species, are grown in Europe. It requires deep, medium heavy, well-drained soil with enough calcium; over-wet or acid soils are not suitable.

For medicinal purposes, the plant can be grown both from seed and by dividing the clumps. Rhubarb for cooking and preserves comes from the related species *Rheum rhabarbarum*.

Dig up the rhizome after the basal leaves have withered in the sixth to seventh year in the case of plants which have been grown from seed, and in the third to fifth year in the case of those vegetatively propagated. Wash, peel and cut the rhizome into pieces about 10 cm (4 in) long and, if necessary, cut in half lengthwise. Dry in the shade at a temperature of up to 50 ° C (122 ° F). The rhizome should retain its original colour. Store in well-sealed containers.

Medicinal Rhubarb may be taken internally for disorders of the digestive system, in small doses for treating diarrhoea, improving the appetite and gastric and intestinal activity, and in larger doses as a laxative and for improving bile production. It should not be taken by anyone with the following conditions: inflamed urinary tract or bladder and kidney stones, especially those formed of calcium oxalate.

Extract for treating diarrhoea: macerate 1 g ($\frac{1}{25}$ oz) dried rhizome in 125 ml (4 $\frac{1}{2}$ fl oz) boiling water. Take three times daily.

Laxative extract: macerate 20 g ($\frac{3}{4}$ oz) dried rhizome in 125 ml (4 $\frac{1}{2}$ oz) boiling water. Take three times daily.

Ribes nigrum L.
Blackcurrant

Saxifragaceae

● This spreading shrub grows to 100–150 cm (39–59 in) height. The annual shoots are thick, glossy, and light yellowish-brown. The bark peels off the older, ash-grey twigs. The alternate, oval, rounded buds are covered with round scales, which are slightly felty with small, yellow oil glands. The leaves are alternate, five- or three-lobed, with the lobes broadly triangular, coarsely toothed and shallowly indented at the petiole. On the underside they have yellow, dot-like glands, the content of which gives the plant its characteristic smell. The bisexual, regular flowers, arranged in groups of four to ten in sparse, drooping bunches, grow on long stalks from the axils of small bracts. The calyx is downy, with yellow glands. It is fused and divided into five lobes, shaped to form a bell or even curved backwards. The petals are linear and dirty white. There are five stamens. The inferior ovary is fused with the calyx. The fruits are globular, glandularly dotted berries, which are green when young and later blackish-violet to black. They ripen in succession.

● Blackcurrant is native to northern Europe and Asia, growing even beyond the Arctic circle. It is widespread in damp woods, alder groves and on river banks. It grows on lowlands and uplands. It is widely cultivated as a fruit bush, the fruits being rich in vitamin C, and often escapes from cultivation.

It is propagated vegetatively from cuttings 20–25 cm (8–10 in) long, cut from shoots in early spring before sprouting. The cuttings take root very well in loose soil. It can also be propagated by rooting the lower branches. It flowers in May.

The fruits have medicinal properties and may be taken raw or dried. Juices, syrups and liqueurs are produced from blackcurrants. In popular healing, dried fruits are mainly used for treating scrofula, coughs, kidney stones, blood in the urine, dropsy and rheumatism of the joints. The fruits have diuretic, astringent, fever-reducing and anti-bacterial properties. The foliage may also be collected, from August to September, as long as it has not been attacked by rusts, which form rusty coloured, bristly growths on the underside of the leaves. Dry the leaves in the shade. Tea made from the dried leaves was formerly used for treating whooping cough in children. Nowadays, the leaves are added to blends for treating coughs and fevers. They are also diuretic.

Rosa centifolia L.
Cabbage Rose

Rosaceae

● This rose forms shrubs up to 3 m (10 ft) high. In has creeping, woody rhizomes, from which new offshoots grow. The stems are erect and curve downwards in an arch in the upper part. They have light green bark, which turns brown on the two-year-old twigs, and prickles which are bent into a marked sickle shape. The buds are alternate, and often reddish in colour. Out of these grow alternate, odd-pinnate leaves with two pairs of lateral, rather slender leaflets. The leaves are dull light green and downy, simply toothed, glandular on the stalk, with the bracts often reddish, and glandularly hairy at the edges. The curved, long, slender, glandular flower stalks bear double, mostly pale pink, fragrant flowers. The calyx lobes (1) are narrow, long and persistent. The hypanthium (swollen stalk beneath the calyx) is oval and the fruits, where these form, are short, oval and light red. Towards autumn the leaves become reddish in colour and persist a long time on the shrubs, especially in the upper parts. The bark of the one-year-old shoots often changes to a reddish colour along one side.

● The Cabbage Rose originates from the Caucasus and several varieties have been cultivated in Europe since the Middle Ages. It flowers from June to August. It is frost-resistant, and so grows at quite high altitudes. In places with higher atmospheric humidity, the small buds turn mouldy and do not open. It flourishes in a warm, sunny location, such as against a south-facing garden wall.

It is propagated very easily from root suckers. These can be replanted in September or October at a distance of 1 m (39 in) apart.

Collect the petals from flowers which have just opened, not from fading ones. They can be used to produce rose oil, which is distilled from the fresh flowers, or they can be dried. For the manufacture of rose oil, collect the flowers in the early morning before the dew dries. Place them in baskets so they will not become squashed. They must be distilled within 12 hours. For drying purposes, collect the petals in dry weather, ideally around noon. Dry them in the shade at a temperature of 25−28 ° C (77−82 ° F). Store in well-sealed containers. The fresh or slightly faded petals may also be preserved in sugar, either to produce 'rose honey', used as an anti-tussive, or special confectionery, which is incidentally good for treating coughs and hoarseness. Cabbage Rose is widely used in popular medicine in the Balkans and in Turkey. An extract made from the petals may be taken for mild diarrhoea.

Extract made with vinegar for use as a gargle or mouth wash: macerate the fresh petals in vinegar for several days, and dilute 15 ml (1 tablespoon) extract with 200 ml (7 fl oz) water.

Rosa gallica L.
French Rose

Rosaceae

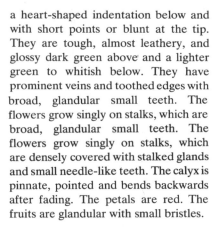

● The French Rose forms a shrub reaching heights of 50—100 cm (20—39 in). Non-flowering twigs, either ascending or growing along the ground, and erect branched flowering shoots grow from the creeping rhizomes. They are covered with thorns of varying shape; some are thick and sickle-shaped, others straight and flattened, while others are dense, needle-like and often glandular. The alternate, odd-pinnate leaves have two pairs of lateral leaflets, some of which over-winter. Glandularly toothed stipules are joined to the lower part of the stalk. The leaflets are oval to almost round, with a heart-shaped indentation below and with short points or blunt at the tip. They are tough, almost leathery, and glossy dark green above and a lighter green to whitish below. They have prominent veins and toothed edges with broad, glandular small teeth. The flowers grow singly on stalks, which are broad, glandular small teeth. The flowers grow singly on stalks, which are densely covered with stalked glands and small needle-like teeth. The calyx is pinnate, pointed and bends backwards after fading. The petals are red. The fruits are glandular with small bristles.

● The French Rose grows in light deciduous woodland, on rocky slopes, and in pastures, thriving mainly on limestone or rocks rich in calcium. It flowers in June and July. It is easy to propagate from root cuttings. Plant the cuttings in September and October at a distance of 50 cm (20 in) apart. In can also be propagated from seeds, which usually germinate only in the second year. Sow in nursery beds in September and October or in March. Replant one-year-old saplings. They flourish both in the sun and in semi-shade.

Collect the flowers in June and July and dry them in thin layers in the shade. Collect the fruits from August to October. Dry them whole in thin layers in the sun. If necessary, complete the drying process with artificial heat. When the flowers are partly dried gently crush them in your hand to remove the calyces, and then rinse with water to remove the surface pulp and the achenes. Wear leather gloves. The majority of the felty hairs are washed off and the pulp with the achenes then dries quickly on its own.

An extract made from the dried flowers is used for treating diarrhoea. A decoction made from the whole fruits or dried pulp may be taken as a tea, being rich in vitamin C. It stimulates digestion and the appetite, has astringent properties, is mildly diuretic and supports bile production. It has reviving effects, particularly in case of fatigue. Mild anti-spasmodic effects have also been recorded. A decoction made only from the achenes is recommended for kidney stones and urinary sand.

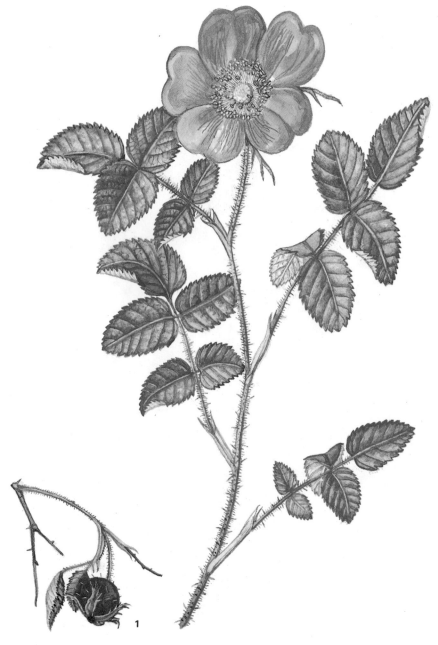

1

Rubus fruticosus L. SPEC. AGGR.
Bramble

Rosaceae

● This thorny shrub grows up to 2 m (6 ½ ft) in height. The annual, non-flowering canes are either arched and growing along the ground or creeping with the ends often taking root. The stems are rounded in the lower part and angled towards the ends. Between the edges they are flat to depressed in furrows, green to reddish-brown and covered with spines which are either erect or bent into a sickle shape. The older branches are brown and glossy. From the alternate, conical, light reddish-brown buds the leaves grow alternately, on the non-flowering stems being palmately pentamerous, and at the tips trimerous with spiny petioles. Their leaflets are oval and toothed. The stipules are linear or narrowly tapering and the stalks flattened to furrowed and spiny. Small spines usually also grow along the main nerves. The blade is glabrous to hairy on the upper side and lighter on the underside. At the ends of the shoots or in the leaf axils bisexual flowers grow in sparse panicles. They have a white or pinkish corolla and a large number of stamens and pistils. The ovaries are fused with the vaulted, white, pulpy receptacle, maturing into globular, bluish-violet to small black drupes – blackberries – joined to the receptacle.

● Bramble grows in woods, riverside hedgerows, on rocky slopes, in clearings and on embankments on lowlands and uplands. It flowers from the end of May until August. It propagates by means of runners from rooted shoots. Seedlings are planted at a distance of 1 m (39 in) apart near wire fences or supports, to which the three or four strongest shoots are tied. These are then shortened by a half, while the weaker shoots are removed. The two-year-old canes are removed in the autumn after harvesting the fruits.

Collect young leaves during the flowering period. Cut them off, together with the petioles, and dry them in thin layers in the shade at a temperature of up to 40–50 °C (104–122 °F). Turn them several times during drying and remove any leaves which are turning yellow or brown. A decoction made from the leaves may be taken as a substi-

tute for tea and the leaves used for this are sometimes fermented. Allow the fresh leaves to fade for 12–24 hours, then press them into a thin layer with a roller, wrap them in cloth and leave at a temperature of 20–45 °C (68–113 °F) for one to two days. During this time, they heat up by themselves, turn brown and acquire a pleasant aroma. The drying process is then completed at a temperature of up to 45 °C (113 °F).

Tea made from the dried fermented leaves is taken for treating diarrhoea and excessive menstrual bleeding. It may also be used as a gargle for treating tonsillitis and bleeding gums. Blackberries are collected while ripe and processed immediately into compotes, jams, syrups, country wines and juices, which are rich in vitamins A and C. They are very beneficial in the diets of convalescents and may be used for treating anaemia.

Rubus idaeus L.
Raspberry

Rosaceae

● A Raspberry shrub is 150–250 cm (59–98 in) high. The erect stems curve in an arch at the tips and branch in the second year. The yellowish-brown, lengthwise furrowed, hairy and finely spiny shoots have brown bark in the second year, and after two years they dry up. The alternate, conical, pointed, light brown buds are covered with bristly scales. The leaves are alternate, some of them trimerous, but mainly odd-pinnate with two to three pairs of lateral leaflets. The leaflets are oval, irregularly and coarsely toothed, sometimes indented into shallow lobes. The blade has short white felt on the underside. The bisexual, drooping flowers grow in sparse panicles in the leaf axils on two-year-old offshoots. The flower stalks are felted. The five triangular sepals bend backwards. The petals are erect, oval and white. There is a large number of stamens and pistils. The fruits are small, red (in cultivated varieties even yellow) drupes clustered on a conical, white receptacle, from which they separate when ripe.

● Raspberry grows on lowlands and uplands in open woodland, in clearings and on heaths. Numerous varieties are cultivated for their fruit. It flowers, depending on position, in June and July.

It is propagated by root suckers, which are planted in rows at a distance of about 50 cm (20 in) apart, ideally near a wire support. Remove weak canes and shorten the strong annual shoots. When the two-year-old canes die off after the fruits have ripened, cut them off at ground level in autumn or winter. The plants require generous feeding in the autumn.

Collect the young leaves either before or during flowering. Dry in thin layers in the shade, so that they retain their original colour. The best leaves are the young ones which have not yet fully opened. These have a high vitamin C content and are used as a substitute for tea.

Raspberry has somewhat astringent properties, having a beneficial effect on the digestive system, smooth uterine muscle and the circulation. Tea made from the leaves is taken mainly for colds, coughs, and feverish illnesses, as well as for headaches and digestive troubles. The ripe fruits are also important. They are dried or processed fresh into juices, syrups, jams and compotes, which have mild laxative properties and are fever-reducing. Collect them in dry weather, in the early morning. They should not come into contact with metal during collecting and subsequent handling. They are used mainly for treating influenza.

● This perennial herb is 20–80 cm (8–31 in) high and has a slanting, branched rhizome and roots which turn woody. The smooth, glabrous, oval, green stem branches out richly from the ground. Later it turns woody in the lower part. The twigs are light green and densely transparently dotted with essential oil capsules. The leaves are alternate, odd-pinnate, and either on short stalks or without stalks, without stipules, with lobed sections which are oval to tapering, entire or finely furrowed and rounded. The light yellow to bluish-green blade is glabrous, thick to pulpy, has a blue bloom on the underside and is dotted with transparent glands. The flowers (1) grow in rich terminal monochasial cymes borne in the axils of simple or three-lobed bracts. They are bisexual, regular and tetra- or pentamerous. The oval, tapering sepals fall after fading. The petals are curved like a spoon, greenish-yellow and dotted with glands. There are eight to ten stamens, which are longer than the petals. The fruit is a capsule with numerous seeds (2).

● Rue originates from the Mediterranean and is cultivated either as a medicinal plant or as a flavouring. It thrives in dry, sunny places in loamy-sandy soil rich in calcium.

It is propagated either by dividing the older clumps or from seeds. Sow the seed 3 cm (1 in) deep in frames in March or April. Plant out the seedlings when they are 10–20 cm (4–8 in) high at the end of May or in June 40 cm (16 in) apart in rows 30 cm (12 in) apart. In harsher weather, protect the plants by covering them with straw manure.

Collect the leaves before flowering or the whole flowering haulm by cutting it off about 10 cm (4 in) above the ground. Dry the leaves quickly in the shade at a temperature of up to 35 °C (95 °F), turning them several times. As the leaves are rather pulpy, drying takes a week or more. Store in the dark in well-sealed containers. During collection and work with Rue, it is wise to wear gloves, as it causes itching or even painful rashes and blisters in sensitive

people. All parts of the plant are poisonous.

Rue contains constituents with a tranquillizing effect on the nervous system and is used to treat spasms in smooth muscle. It also has mild diuretic properties and stimulates the appetite. It increases the firmness of the blood vessels

and reduces bleeding from small blood vessels. Excessive doses can cause inflammation of the digestive system and kidneys, dizziness and symptoms of general nausea or even hallucination. Rue is poisonous and should never be used in home medicines.

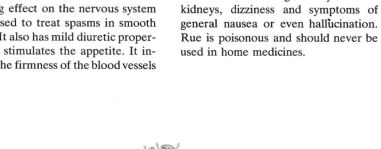

Salix alba L.
White Willow

Salicaceae

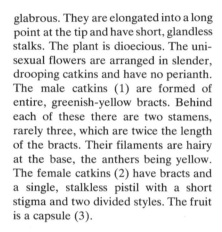

● This tree reaches heights of up to 28 m (92 ft) and the trunk is more than 1 m (39 in) in diameter. The bark, which is smooth and greyish-brown when young, later changes into a lengthwise fissured outer bark. The annual shoots are slender and pliant, yellowish-brown to reddish-brown, with silky felt at the tip. The older twigs are brown and shiny. The alternate, elongated, pointed, flattened buds are each covered with a single enveloping scale, which is yellow to reddish-brown. The leaves are alternate, tapering and finely toothed, with silky hair on the underside when young, later being almost glabrous. They are elongated into a long point at the tip and have short, glandless stalks. The plant is dioecious. The unisexual flowers are arranged in slender, drooping catkins and have no perianth. The male catkins (1) are formed of entire, greenish-yellow bracts. Behind each of these there are two stamens, rarely three, which are twice the length of the bracts. Their filaments are hairy at the base, the anthers being yellow. The female catkins (2) have bracts and a single, stalkless pistil with a short stigma and two divided styles. The fruit is a capsule (3).

● White Willow grows throughout almost the whole of Europe on riverbanks, alluvial deposits and in damp woodland on lowlands and uplands. It is often planted by running water or is cultivated for the production of wicker for basket-making. It flowers in April and May and is propagated vegetatively from hardwood cuttings. The thick branches also take root well when pushed into damp soil. It grows quickly, will tolerate even lengthy flooding and is frost-resistant.

Collect the bark from two- to three-year-old branches in March and at the beginning of April. Cut two circles in the bark of the twigs at a distance of 20–30 cm (8–12 in), and join them with a lengthwise cut. Tap the bark with a blunt instrument and peel it off. Dry it either in the sun or by artificial heat. The leaves and young shoots are also used in popular healing.

Decoctions and extracts made from the bark may be taken for treating fevers and inflammation, and as a tranquillizer and haemostatic. It is used mainly for treating rheumatic disorders of the joints, gout, gastric ulcers, diarrhoea, inflammation of the digestive system and some nervous disorders. It may be applied externally to reduce excessive sweating, on compresses on wounds and skin ulcers and used as a gargle. A decoction made from the leaves in vinegar is used as a mouth rinse to treat bad breath. A decoction made from the whole canes with the leaves is added to baths for treating rheumatism.

V–VI, IX

V–VI

Salvia officinalis L.
Sage

Labiatae

● Sage is a semi-shrub up to 70 cm (28 in) in height. The stems are either erect or ascending, woody in the lower part and richly branched, so that the older plants form bushy, small shrublike clumps. The tips are herbaceous with a woolly felt, almost rotund and often tinted purple. In the leaf axils grow short lateral twigs. The leaves are opposite, on long stalks, oval or tapering, finely toothed, and partly survive the winter. The blade is often indented in a heart shape at the stalk, sometimes having two small earlets at the base. The leaves are either round at the tips or with blunt points, and a dull green to silvery grey colour, with dense, net-like veins particularly conspicuous on the underside. It gives off a pleasant smell when rubbed. The flowers (1), which are arranged in racemes, occur only on the two-year-old shoots. The calyx is brownish-red and has soft hair, the corolla being symmetrical, two-lipped and bluish-violet, or rarely white. In the mouth of the corolla there is a circle of hairs. There are only two stamens and the style is divided into two unequal parts. From the superior ovary develop four black nutlets.

● Sage is native to the Balkans and the Mediterranean. It requires dryish soils rich in calcium and a sheltered position, growing both in full sunlight and semi-shade. It flowers in June and July.

It is propagated either from seeds or vegetatively. Sow the seeds in autumn from October to November or in February to March, 2–3 cm ($\frac{3}{4}$–1 in) deep in a frame. Plant out the seedlings in May 40 cm (16 in) apart in rows 30 cm (12 in) apart. It may also be propagated from cuttings taken in the spring, and by dividing the clumps. In harsh weather, protect the plants from freezing by covering the clumps with earth.

Collect the leaves or the entire soft annual shoots in May and June. The leaves can also be harvested a second time in September. Dry spread out in thin layers in the shade at a temperature of up to 35 °C (95 °F). Store in well-sealed containers. Essential oils are obtained industrially from Sage.

Sage has excellent anti-bacterial properties and is effective in treating many types of inflammation. It stimulates the activity of the digestive tract and the appetite, as well as bile production. It relieves flatulence and spasms, is fever-reducing and is used in the treatment of diabetes. It is taken in the form of an extract made with hot water. It also has astringent properties and so is used as a mouth wash to heal bleeding gums. Excessive doses of Sage are dangerous and it should not be taken by nursing mothers as it is suspected of inhibiting milk production. The essential oils must never be used in popular healing, as even small doses are poisonous.

1

153

Sambucus ebulus L.
Dwarf Elder

Caprifoliaceae

VI—VIII

VIII

X—XI

● Dwarf Elder is a perennial herb with an unpleasant smell. The richly branched rhizome penetrates large areas. Numerous erect, unbranched, 150—200 cm (59—79 in) tall stems grow from it. They are cylindrical, furrowed and either glabrous or with scattered hair. The leaves are opposite, stalked and odd-pinnate, with two to four pairs of lateral leaflets, which are elongated, often asymmetrical in the lower part, pointed, sharply toothed, glabrous above and woolly on the underside. They have stipules at the stalk. These are oval to tapering, toothed in the lower leaves, and linear in the upper ones. The flowers are arranged in richly branched, dense corymbs. These have a five-pointed calyx and a corolla (1) consisting of five white or reddish, oval, pointed petals which are bent downwards. There are five stamens. The anthers are purplish reddish-violet. The pistil has three styles which are sessile on the ovary. The ovary matures into glossy black, small oval drupes growing on violet stalks. Each of the drupes contains three triangular seeds.

● Dwarf Elder grows in clearings, on dumping grounds, in ditches, along road embankments, on shrubby slopes, and on the edges of woods. It often grows in masses covering large areas. It flowers from June to August.

The main parts used are the rhizomes and fruits and, occasionally, the leaves or the whole flowering haulm. Collect the fruits when they are fully ripe from August onwards. Either dry them in artificial heat so that they do not go mouldy while being dried, or preserve them by bottling. They are occasionally fermented to make wine. Dig up the rhizomes in the autumn. Clean them thoroughly and remove the green, slender parts and small roots. Cut the thicker parts lengthwise and dry at a temperature of up to 50 °C (122 °F). The dried foliage, flowers or whole flowering tops with the upper leaves are only rarely used in popular healing. They are dried in the shade.

The fruits have diuretic and fever-reducing properties and also promote bile production. They have been used in popular healing to treat dropsy, coughs and kidney disorders. However, they are mildly poisonous and larger doses can cause severe diarrhoea and vomiting. They should therefore never be used in home medicines. The rhizomes have similar properties to the fruits and are most usually used as decoctions for gargling to treat sore throats or as a mouth rinse to relieve toothache. They may be added to the bath to treat colds and rheumatic pain in the joints. The leaves and flowers are used in popular medicine for illnesses connected with colds.

1

Sambucus nigra L.
Elder

Caprifoliaceae

● This wide-branched shrub or tree grows to heights of up to 10 m (33 ft). The trunk has a diameter of up to 30 cm (12 in). The bark, which is light grey when young, later changes into a coarse, grey outer bark with lengthwise furrowing. The annual shoots are thick and light greyish-brown, the older branches brown. There is white pith inside the branches. The opposite, oval, pointed buds are covered in the lower part only with reddish-brown scales, from which the green leaf buds protrude. The leaves are opposite, odd-pinnate and petiolate with two or three pairs of lateral leaflets. These are oval to tapering and coarsely toothed, usually narrowing downwards into a wedge shape, and entire. The stalk has small glandular stipules at the base. The flowers are bisexual and arranged in rich, flat cymes. They have a short, bell-shaped calyx and a rounded corolla composed of white or yellowish oval petals. There are five stamens. The ovary has a sessile stigma divided into three to five lobes, maturing into globular, glossy, blackish-violet drupes with three flat seeds each.

● Elder is common throughout almost the whole of Europe, growing abundantly on lowlands and uplands as undergrowth in humous coniferous and deciduous woodland, on dumping grounds, in hedgerows, abandoned parks and gardens, on river banks, paths, rubbish heaps and other waste ground. It flowers in June, sometimes even until July.

Cut off the inflorescences with scissors in dry weather and place them loosely in a basket. Leave them to fade. Pull the flowers off the stalks and dry in thin layers in the shade. They must retain their original colour. Store in well-sealed containers. They have

diuretic and fever-reducing properties and act as tranquillizers. An extract made with hot water may be taken for coughs, feverish illnesses, tonsillitis, dropsy and constipation. It may also be used as a gargle and forms part of tranquillizing teas.

Collect the ripe fruits from September to October. Either dry them by artificial heat or process them into jams

and syrups or ferment them into wine. The fresh fruits have laxative properties, the dried fruits having the opposite effect. The extract has diuretic properties and markedly reduces pain caused by inflammation of the nerves and nerve roots after chills and so on.

Do not take excessive doses of Elder as it has unpleasant side-effects, causing retching and diarrhoea.

Extract for treating colds: scald 10 ml (2 teaspoons) dried elderberries in 200 ml (7 fl oz) boiling water, macerate and filter.

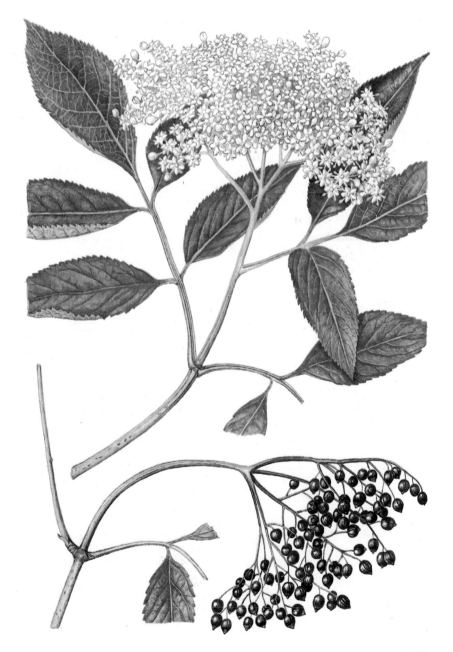

Sambucus nigra

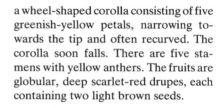

Sambucus racemosa L.
Red-berried Elder

Caprifoliaceae

● This shrub or small tree, which is 1−4 m (3−13 ft) in height, has dark brown bark, which changes, when old, into a lengthwise fissured outer bark. The annual shoots are thick, greyish-brown and often arched. Inside there is a wide, cylindrical, rusty brown pith. The buds are opposite and globular with brown-bordered green scales. The terminal buds usually grow in pairs. The leaves are opposite, stalked and odd-pinnate, with two or three pairs of lateral leaflets. They have long points, are coarsely toothed at the edges, glabrous on the upper side and finely woolly on the underside. The flowers, grouped in dense, oval panicles, appear before the leaves sprout and have a floury smell. They are tiny and bisexual, with a short, tubular calyx and a wheel-shaped corolla consisting of five greenish-yellow petals, narrowing towards the tip and often recurved. The corolla soon falls. There are five stamens with yellow anthers. The fruits are globular, deep scarlet-red drupes, each containing two light brown seeds.

● Red-berried Elder grows in upland and mountain forests, woodland, in clearings, on shrubby slopes and sometimes even on rocks. It flowers in April and May. The fruits ripen in July and August, as late as September in higher locations.

Collect only the ripe fruits. Either use them fresh or dry them at a temperature of up to 45 °C (113 °F).

They contain vitamins C and B_1, as well as anti-bacterial constituents, which check the development of some other micro-organisms in the digestive tract and some microscopic fungi. Extracts can be made from the fruits by dipping the whole panicle of ripe fruits into boiling water for a short time. The extract may be sweetened and taken as a tea substitute. It reduces fever and has mild laxative effects. The seeds are poisonous but the poison is not released by macerating or scalding the fresh fruits, nor by boiling the dry fruits for a very short time. Therefore, excessive doses can cause vomiting and Red-berried Elder should be used with extreme care in home medicines. In spring, an extract made from the dried fruits may be taken for additional vitamin C as a pick-me-up. It may be drunk hot as a tea, or cold as a slightly sour juice. In Spain, a decoction made from the bark is taken as a diuretic and in Romania, the sap from the shrubs is collected in early spring for making an ointment to treat cuts.

Syrup from the fresh fruits: press the fruits, leave the juice to stand, filter and simmer with double the quantity of sugar.

Laxative decoction: boil 10 g ($\frac{2}{5}$ oz) ground fruits in 150 ml (5 fl oz) water for five minutes.

Sanguisorba officinalis L.
Great Burnet

Rosaceae

● Great Burnet is a perennial herb with a stem 40–90 cm (16–35 in) in height. The rhizome is thick with short branches, cylindrical, bent or even twisted, brown, yellowish in cross-section with a reddish centre. A rosette of basal leaves on long stalks grows from it. The leaves are erect and odd-pinnate with four to six pairs of lateral, stalked leaflets. The leaflets are oval with a heart-shaped indentation at the base, round at the ends, coarsely toothed, dark green and glossy on the upper side and paler with prominent veins underneath. Erect, sparsely branched, furrowed, glabrous stems grow from the rhizome and have three to four alternate leaves. The stems terminate in dark red, oval flower heads which flower in stages from the base upwards. The flowers have only a dark, brownish-red, four-toothed calyx, with no corolla. The four stamens bear yellow anthers on long red filaments. The inferior ovary with its filamentous style matures into a single-seeded achene enclosed in a winged calyx.

● Great Burnet grows in damp meadows and fens on lowlands and uplands. It is common in north England and the Midlands. It flowers from July to September.

Dig up the rhizomes, either in early spring or in autumn after the flowers have faded. Use rhizomes from plants that are several years old. Dry them in the shade. If they are dried in artificial heat, the temperature should not exceed 40 °C (104 °F). Before drying, remove the small roots and slender lateral twigs and rinse the rhizome in water. Store in dry conditions in well-sealed containers. In popular healing the whole haulm is also used. Collect it while it is in flower.

An extract made from the rhizome may be taken for haemorrhaging and diarrhoea. It is thought to have anti-bacterial properties. In popular healing in Romania, alcohol extracts made from the haulm are popular for treating digestive disorders, especially spasms and pains in the abdomen. Similarly, the cleaned rhizomes may be steeped in spirit and the extract used for treating gastric pain and loss of appetite. Children are given a decoction made from the flowering haulm for diarrhoea. Great Burnet may be used to treat various types of internal bleeding, bleeding diarrhoea and excessive menstrual bleeding. However, these are all conditions requiring proper medical advice. It may be applied externally on compresses after injuries, in drops for nose-bleeds and as a mouth rinse for bleeding gums.

Extract for diarrhoea with bleeding, haemorrhoids, after menstruation, and so on: macerate 10–15 ml (2–3 teaspoons) ground dried rhizomes in 500 ml (18 fl oz) cold water for eight hours. Take in small doses during the day.

157

Saponaria officinalis L.
Soapwort

Dianthaceae

● This perennial herb reaches heights of 50−80 cm (20−31 in). It has a jointed, creeping, richly branched, cylindrical rhizome (1) often spreading over large areas. Large numbers of erect, rotund, glabrous, sterile or flower-bearing stems grow from it. The non-flowering stems are simple, with oval to elongated and pointed, oppositely arranged leaves. The lower ones are on short petioles, the upper ones sessile, either with short hair or almost glabrous and rough at the edges, with three prominent veins. The flower-bearing stems are sparsely branched and leafy in the lower part and terminate in rich panicles of flowers. In the leaf axils are often situated small bunches of small leaves and in the upper part several flowers. The flowers grow on short stalks, are regular and bisexual. The green or reddish, hairy calyx is divided at the top into five oval teeth. The light pink or white corolla is divided into five flatly spreading, shallowly indented petals. There are 10 stamens, and the fruit is an oval capsule.

● Soapwort grows in riverside hedgerows, in damp sandy soil, often even along road and railway embankments and waysides, on dumping grounds and in other uncultivated places. Its double forms are grown in gardens, although it can easily turn wild and become a weed. It has a marked tolerance of drought. It flowers from June to September. It can easily be propagated from parts of the rhizomes as well as from seed. For better development of the rhizomes, prevent the plants from flowering by pinching out flower buds at the tip of the stems.

Dig up the rhizome in autumn or in early spring. Remove the aerial parts and rinse quickly in water. Dry as quickly as possible in the sun or by artificial heat at a temperature of 40−50 °C (104−122 °F). Store tied in bundles. The haulm may also be used. Dry, without turning, in thin layers in the shade.

An extract may be taken internally as an expectorant, fever-reducing agent and for respiratory ailments. It also has diuretic properties. The long-term use of Soapwort causes unpleasant side-effects (gastric irritation). The haulm has the same medicinal properties. An extract made from the fresh haulm may be added to baths for treating skin disorders and eczema.

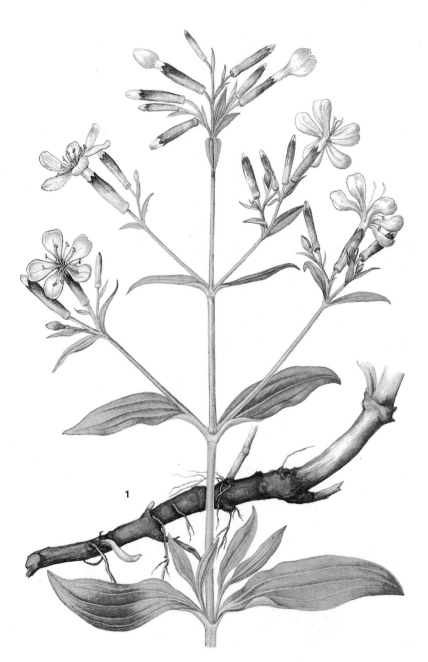

> **Extract for respiratory ailments:** macerate 5 ml (1 teaspoon) ground root in 400 ml (14 fl oz) cold water. Take in spoonfuls during the day.

Saxifraga granulata L.
Meadow Saxifrage

Saxifragaceae

● Meadow Saxifrage is a perennial herb reaching a height of up to 30 cm (12 in). It has a dense clump of fine, branched rootlets. A rosette of basal leaves grows from this. In the axils of the basal leaves are numerous globular or oval, pointed small tubers covered in reddish-brown skin. The basal leaves are kidney-shaped, coarsely toothed to lobed, and glandular-hairy. The blade, which is notched to heart-shaped at the base, narrows abruptly into the stalk, which is several times longer than the blade. The stalk is depressed into a fur-row and widened in the lower part. The erect downy stem is sparsely leafed and sparsely branched. The stem leaves are alternate, the lower ones being long-stalked, the upper ones sessile, and are oval to elongated and lobed. The flowers (1) grow on glandular stalks in the axils of linear bracts. The densely glandular calyx is joined to the semi-inferior ovary, being divided in the upper part into five blunt lobes. The petals are white and oval in outline. The 10 stamens, arranged in two circles, bear yellow anthers. The ovary matures into a broadly oval capsule.

● Meadow Saxifrage grows in non-calcareous soil in meadows and pas-tures, on grassy and stony slopes, on the edges of forests, in woodland clearings and on quite shady rocks. It flowers from May to August. Double-flowered forms are cultivated in gardens. It is propagated by means of propagating tubers. Plant them in early spring in light garden soil with no calcium content. Sow the seeds in a cold frame after the capsules have matured. Plant out the seedlings in beds.

Collect the flowering haulm from May to July and dry it as quickly as possible in the shade in an airy place. Store in well-sealed containers.

Meadow Saxifrage has excellent diuretic properties and is also said to help dissolve kidney stones. Because of its expectorant properties, it was for-merly also used for treating respiratory diseases. It is rarely used on its own but forms part of diuretic teas, blended for example with Knotgrass, Mint and Birch leaves. It may be combined with plants which stimulate gall bladder ac-tivity and liver regeneration, such as Celandine and Milk Thistle.

Extract for uroliths: macerate 10 ml (2 teaspoons) dried haulm in 200 ml (7 fl oz) water. Take the extract two to three times daily.

159

Silybum marianum (L.) GAERTN.
Milk Thistle

Compositae

● This is a stout, decorative, biennial herb (annual in a temperate climate). It grows to heights of 60–150 cm (24–59 in). A basal rosette of leaves grows from the thick, branched taproot. These are oval, up to 30 cm (12 in) in length, wavy-lobed, coarsely and unevenly toothed at the edges with prickly spines, tough, glossy green and with white blotches along the veins. In the second year an erect, tough stem grows. It is sparsely branched in the upper part, glossy, and covered with a thin, web-like felt. The tops of the stems are sparsely leafed, the lower parts densely leafed. The stem leaves are alternate and with-out stalks, the upper ones have heart-shaped indentations and are clasping, oval and with yellow spines at the edges. Single flower heads grow at the branch tips, their glabrous, spiny toothed bracts terminating in a large spine which is depressed into a furrow and bends backwards. The flowers (1) are reddish-violet, rarely white. The fruits are glabrous, brown, blotched achenes with a circle of glossy white down at the top (2).

● Milk Thistle is native to the Mediterranean and some parts of Asia. It has been cultivated in other parts of Europe from the earliest times, occasionally turning wild along waysides, on dumping grounds, stony slopes, waste ground and other infertile types of soil. It flowers from July to September. It is propagated from the achenes, which are sown in autumn in a warm location. They germinate within a week. In mountain regions, plants grown from a spring sowing flower in the same year, but the fruits do not mature. Therefore, it is better to sow the seeds in autumn. Sow them in rows 60 cm (24 in) apart. Thin the seedlings to 60 cm (24 in).

The ripe fruits have medicinal properties. Cut off the mature flower heads and dry them. Shake out the fruits.

Milk Thistle fruits are processed by the pharmaceutical industry into drops and coated tablets. In popular healing, a decoction is prepared from them. These contain constituents thought to increase bile production, reduce fever and have beneficial effects on liver activity and the nervous system of the intestines. A decoction may be taken to treat jaundice, gallstones associated with colic, acute and chronic inflammation of the liver and cirrhosis of the liver. It is used as an auxiliary medicine in conjunction with a prescribed diet and medical treatment. It may also be applied externally to haemorrhoids, varicose veins and leg abscesses.

Solanum dulcamara L.
Bittersweet

Solanaceae

● This semi-shrub is either creeping or climbing and may grow to heights of up to 200 cm (79 in). The rhizome is creeping and branched with numerous small root clumps. The stems, which are woody in the lower part and herbaceous in the upper part, are glabrous, somewhat angled, and either grow along the ground or climb up other plants. The leaves are alternate, stalked and variously shaped. Most often they are oval, tapering, pointed and indented in a heart shape at the stalk. The upper leaves are either narrowly heart-shaped or triangular, often with one or two separate oval sections on the stalk. Sometimes they are even trimerous, entire and with scattered hair on both sides. The mostly drooping flowers grow either in lateral or terminal panicles composed of monochasial cymes. They grow on long stalks and are bisexual and almost regular, having a perennial calyx which is divided into five lobes. The star-shaped corolla consists of five, more rarely of four, oval tapering, pointed petals which are dark bluish-violet in colour. In the lower part they have two green blotches with white borders. The five stamens have yellow anthers. The superior ovary matures into a glossy red, oval berry (1).

● Bittersweet grows on river banks, in fens, on the banks of ponds and lakes, damp clearings, hedges and woods, sometimes growing even out of rotting wood in the hollows of old, decayed willows or poplars. It grows on lowlands and highlands. Double-flowered or variously coloured varieties with flowers which can be white, flesh-red, blue or with yellow blotches are cultivated in gardens.

It is propagated either from cuttings or seeds. As the fruit pulp retards germination, the crushed berries are soaked in water for 24 hours. The seeds are sown into damp, humous soil and the seedlings are planted out into rows 50 cm (20 in) apart in permanently damp places near wire netting or supporting structures.

The two- and three-year-old stalks are harvested, either before sprouting or in the autumn after the leaves have fallen. The thicker stalks are halved and dried quickly.

Bittersweet has diuretic and reviving effects, stimulates the metabolism and checks the reproduction of bacteria. Medicines for treating gallbladder diseases are manufactured from it. Bittersweet is poisonous and should never be used in home medicines.

1

161

Solidago virgaurea L.
Goldenrod

Compositae

● This is a perennial plant up to 100 cm (39 in) tall. The rhizome is short, sometimes many-headed, notched at the base with an abundance of slender root hairs. Rosettes of basal leaves grow from it. They are oval, narrowing into a wedge shape towards the base, pointed, finely toothed at the edges and glabrous. The stem is erect, richly leafed, rounded, furrowed, often glabrous and tinged violet at the base and sometimes with sparse, fine felt at the top. The stem leaves are alternate and oval to tapering, the lower ones being stalked, the upper ones sessile and tapering. The stem terminates in a dense, cylindrical to conical raceme or a branched, rich panicle of flower heads. The flower heads have several rows of linear tapering bracts with broad, leathery borders. The edge of the flower head is formed only by female, strap-shaped florets (1) which are linear and twice as long as the involucre. In the centre there are bisexual, tubular flowers (2). The fruits are elongatedly oval, finely hairy achenes with a honeycomb structure and down at the top (3).

● Goldenrod grows in open woodland, on shrubby slopes, on heaths and on rocks. It flowers from July to September. Double-flowered or dwarf forms are cultivated in gardens. It is propagated either by dividing the clumps or from seeds, but these have a low rate of germination. Sow the seed from April to June in a cold frame, where it germinates within two weeks. Plant out the seedlings 20 cm (8 in) apart. The plant thrives both in the sun and in semi-shade, and is not demanding in its soil requirements.

Cut off the whole flowering haulm at about half the plant's height. Dry in small bundles in the shade or in drying sheds hung up on wires, at a temperature of around 40 °C (104 °F). The leaves and flowers must retain their original colour. Store in well-sealed containers.

It has astringent and diuretic properties, promotes sweating and has antibacterial properties. It also increases the firmness of fine blood vessels in both mucous membrane and the skin. An extract may be taken internally to treat chronic kidney inflammation, water retention, metabolic disorders and diarrhoea. It may be used as a mouth wash or gargle and may be applied externally on compresses on skin abscesses or slow-healing wounds.

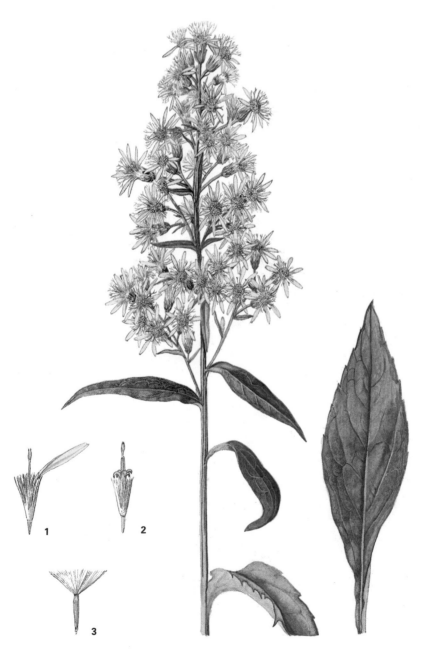

Extract: macerate 10–15 g ($\frac{2}{5}$–$\frac{1}{2}$ oz) dried haulm in 250 ml (9 fl oz) water and take in three doses during the day.

Sorbus aucuparia L.
Rowan, Mountain Ash

Rosaceae

● This tree, with an oval crown, grows to heights of up to 20 m (66 ft). The bark remains smooth and greyish brown for a long time, only changing in old age into an outer bark which peels off in smooth, papery plates. The erect, glossy, reddish-brown shoots have an ash-grey coating, the older twigs being grey to blackish-grey. The buds are alternate, oval to elongatedly cylindrical, and covered with reddish-violet scales with silky hair. The terminal buds are markedly larger than the appressed lateral buds. The lateral twigs are shortened, crooked and with circular to knotty ridging. The leaves are alternate and odd-pinnate, with four to seven pairs of lateral, longish-oval, coarsely toothed leaflets. The flowers, borne in rich corymbose panicles, have five sepals, five white petals, 15−20 stamens and a pistil with two to five stigmas. The fruits are bright red, globular pomes (1) with two to four seeds.

● Rowan is distributed throughout the whole of Europe as far as the northern polar forest border, growing on lowlands and uplands in woods and on moors. It is often cultivated in parks and gardens, and the sweet-fruited varieties are grown for the fruit. It is propagated easily from seeds, which are obtained by soaking the ripe fruits in water and sowing them in nurseries. The sweet-fruited varieties have to be grafted. The most valuable variety is the ssp. *moravica*, also known as the variety 'Dulcis', which has larger fruits lacking the astringent taste.

The fruits have medicinal properties and are either processed fresh or dried. Collect them in September and October in sunny weather and dry either in the sun or at a temperature of up to 50 °C (122 °F).

The fruits have diuretic, mild laxative and astringent properties. Therefore, they are used in popular healing as a diuretic preparation for treating kidney stones and rheumatism, as a preparation for regulating intestinal activity and as a means of stimulating urine excretion in children. The fruits are also effective in cases of inflammation of the upper respiratory passages. The juice from fresh rowanberries or rowanberry preserve may be used.

Rowanberry juice as a diuretic preparation: crush 5 ml (1 teaspoon) rowanberries and macerate in 500 ml (18 fl oz) cold water. Take several times daily.

Rowanberry preserve: simmer 1 kg (2 lb 3 oz) rowanberries with 500 g (1 lb 2 oz) sugar. Take 5 ml (1 teaspoon) several times daily.

1

Symphytum officinale L.
Common Comfrey

Boraginaceae

● This perennial, stout herb, 60–100 cm (24–39 in) in height, has a perpendicular, multi-headed, beetroot-like thickened rhizome (1), from which grow black, finger-thick, branched roots. The stem is erect, tough, branched at the top, with spreading, rough, bristly hairs. The leaves are alternate, oval tapering and narrow gradually towards the base into a winged stalk and extend down the stem. At the tip the leaves are pointed, with prominent small veins underneath, and very rough. The stalked, drooping, regular bisexual flowers grow at the ends of branches in dense, double monochasia. The tubular, funnel-shaped calyx is up to a half or two-thirds divided into five tough, tapering teeth which are pointed at the tips. The dingy reddish-violet, rarely white corolla is shallowly divided into five broad, three-sided lobes which bend outwards, thus forming a narrow border. At the mouth they have three-sided, short, scaly protuberances. The five stamens have dark violet anthers which are longer than the filaments. The fruits are four greyish-brown nutlets.

● Common Comfrey is widespread in damp meadows, ditches, on the banks of both stagnant and running water and in damp undergrowth. It grows on lowlands and uplands. It flowers from May to July.

Dig up the rhizomes, together with the roots, from spring until the beginning of summer. Wash, cut lengthwise and dry in moderate heat. Store in well-sealed containers because they easily become damp again.

They contain constituents which affect the circulation and are mildly laxative. Common Comfrey is rarely taken internally, but may be used as a laxative and to treat coughs and a build-up of phlegm in the respiratory passages. It is mainly used externally on compresses to relieve bruises, inflamed veins, chronic disorders of the joints and bones, varicose veins and leg abscesses. It was formerly used for treating fractures.

1

Decoction for compresses and for rinsing the mouth to treat bleeding gums: boil 50 g (1 $\frac{3}{4}$ oz) rhizome in 500 ml (18 fl oz) water for 10 minutes. Soak compresses in the warm decoction for ulcers and the cold decoction for bruises.

III–IV

 III–IV

 V

Taraxacum officinale WIGGERS
Dandelion

Compositae

● The Dandelion is a widely distributed perennial weed. It has a short, often multi-headed, brown rhizome with scaly remnants of died-off leaves. A spindle-shaped, sparsely branched, pulpy brown root grows from it. This exudes an abundance of white, bitter latex when it is cut. Rosettes of basal leaves grow at the apexes of the rhizomes. These are simple, tapering to elongated, coarsely and irregularly toothed and with lobed indentation, narrowing into a broad, sometimes reddish petiole. From the rosette of basal leaves grow several hollow, cylindrical stalks, terminating in single, large flower heads which close at night or during rain. These have a three-rowed involucre composed of linear tapering, greyish-green bracts, often with a narrow white border. Inside the flower head there are about 200 strap-shaped, bisexual florets, which are golden-yellow and sometimes a little reddish or brownish underneath. The receptacle is glabrous and non-paleaceous. The fruits are spindle-shaped, greyish-brown achenes which narrow into a small beak with white, umbrella-like down.

● Dandelion is very common in bare and grassy places and frequently occurs in fields and gardens. It grows on lowlands and uplands. It flowers abundantly at the beginning of May and again, though to a lesser extent, in autumn.

The rhizome together with the roots and the basal rosettes of leaves are used in popular healing. Collect them before flowering in March and April. Dig up the plants carefully, so that the roots are as little damaged as possible. Clean off the soil, rinse quickly in water and dry, slowly at first so that they fade, and then complete the drying process by artificial heat up to a temperature of 50 °C (122 °F). The leaves should retain their original green colour and the roots should be crumbly, yellow inside with concentric circles of dark glands with brown dried latex. Store in sealed containers or plastic bags, protected from moisture and insects. The leaves and flowers may also be collected in spring. Dry only the ligulate florets, having removed the receptacle and involucre,

in a thin layer. The florets can also be picked in sunny weather directly from the flower heads.

An extract made from the roots and flowers stimulates the production and excretion of bile, the appetite, the activity of the digestive system and the metabolism and has diuretic properties.

Dandelion tea is also said to have beneficial effects in mild cases of diabetes. The dried rhizome is also used for treating haemorrhoids. Leaves picked before flowering are rich in vitamin C and do not taste bitter. They can be eaten as a salad.

Teucrium chamaedrys L.
Wall Germander

Labiatae

● A semi-shrub 15–30 cm (6–12 in) in height with a dense network of slender, branched rhizomes, from which grow dense clumps of ascending stems. The perpendicular roots, which tend to turn woody, and the fine rootlets penetrate the ground. The stems grow along the ground and take root easily. They are branched, densely leafed and bear numerous glandular hairs, are cylindrical and articulate. They bear opposite, oval, short-stalked leaves, which are toothed at the margin and softly downy on both sides. The blade is dark green and glossy above and greyish-green underneath. The leaves overwinter. The symmetrical, stalked flowers (1) are arranged in spiky inflorescences. The lower flowers grow in the leaf axils, which gradually change towards the top of the stem into smaller, narrower, stemless bracts. The tubular bell-shaped, often purplish calyx is divided into five hairy teeth of equal size. The corolla (2) is pink with a violet tinge, rarely white, and double-lipped, with the lower lip woolly on the outside. The tube is glabrous. The stamens terminate in brown anthers. The fruits are glabrous nutlets.

● Wall Germander grows in warm positions on dry slopes, rocks (mainly calcite), screes, old walls and embankments. The densely hairy or grey-felted varieties are also cultivated in gardens. These are propagated from the rooting stems. It flowers in July and August.

Cut off the flowering haulm at ground level and dry in the shade at a temperature of up to 40 °C (104 °F). The dried haulm has a pleasant smell.

A decoction of Wall Germander has beneficial effects on the digestive system, stimulates the appetite and the formation of gastric juices, promotes sweating and reduces fever. It has diuretic properties and is also used for treating gout. It contains vitamin C and so may be used during convalescence after infectious, feverish illnesses and as a pick-me-up. In popular healing, it may also be taken internally to treat chest pain, feverish chills, toothache and inflammatory gum disorders. The decoction may be applied externally on compresses on slow-healing wounds or added to baths for treating haemorrhoids. For digestive troubles, diarrhoea and stomach-ache, Wall Germander may be combined with the haulm of Milfoil and given as a decoction or extract in wine. This combination also has reviving effects.

> **Decoction for loss of appetite, digestive troubles and diarrhoea:** pour 250 ml (9 fl oz) boiling water over 15 ml (1 tablespoon) dried haulm and leave to macerate for 15 minutes. Take 200 ml (7 fl oz) decoction before meals.

Thymus pulegioides L.
Large Thyme

Labiatae

● This is a perennial, aromatic herb or a semi-shrub 5–30 cm (2–12 in) in height. Numerous rooting stems grow along the ground from the spindle-shaped root. They are sparsely tufted and turn woody in the lower part. From these grow ascending twigs of two types: the shorter ones are non-flowering, densely leafed, and the higher ones, which often branch out further, are leafed in the lower part and terminate in an inflorescence. The stems are square, and covered at the edges with short, bent hairs. The leaves on the flower-bearing stalks are of approximately the same size. They are round, oval or even elongated, bristly on and along the petiole, sometimes glabrous. The flowers are arranged in cylindrical heads which are sparse in the lower part. The calyx is tubular bell-shaped and the corolla two-lipped and purple-red or white. The fruits are brown nutlets.

● Large Thyme grows on pastures and in open woodland in sunny spots, flourishing on lowlands and uplands. It flowers from June to August. Various forms are cultivated: ones with white- and yellow-blotched, almost golden yellow leaves or with white, pink or fiery red flowers. It is easy to propagate, either from runners taken from the rooting stems or from seed. The seed is sown in April and germinates within two weeks.

Collect both the flowering and the non-flowering twigs, together with the leaves, but without the basal woody parts of the stem. Remove grass blades, woody pieces and other unwanted material and dry, without turning, in a thin layer in the shade. If you use artificial heat, the temperature should not exceed 40 °C (104 °F). Store in well-sealed containers. Other species of Thyme are considered to be of equal value in home medicines.

Large Thyme contains constituents which are anti-inflammatory and expectorant, stimulate the appetite and gastric juice formation and relieve spasms. An extract made with boiling water may be used for treating bronchitis, sore throats, loss of appetite and various digestive troubles, insufficient gastric juices, flatulence, and diarrhoea. It may be used as a mouth rinse and gargle to treat bleeding gums and on compresses on inflamed skin.

Thymus vulgaris L.
Garden Thyme

Labiatae

● Garden Thyme is a richly branched semi-shrub 20–30 cm (8–12 in) in height. The erect branches are markedly woody in the lower part. Herbaceous shoots, which are downy over the whole surface, grow from these. The leaves are opposite, short-stalked, oval to tapering or almost kite-shaped, round at the corners and conspicuously inrolled at the edges. The blade is glabrous and densely dotted with glands on the upper side, having hairs or thin white felt on the underside. The leaf margins are either entire or imperceptibly toothed. Bunches of other, small leaves often grow on the axils of the short-stalked leaves. In the axils of the upper leaves there are clustered flowers in groups of three to six. Sparse, spiky inflorescences also form at the stem tips. The calyx is of an open bell shape, two-lipped, and has short hairs (1). The two-lipped pink and violet corolla (2) has a flat and almost undivided upper lip, the lower one being divided into three lobes. The four stamens protrude far from the corolla. The stigma is divided into two. The fruits are nutlets.

● Garden Thyme is native to the Mediterranean, and is widely cultivated in gardens, both as a culinary herb and as an ornamental plant. Several varieties with blotched leaves or with clustered elongated inflorescences are grown. It flourishes in warm positions in light, sandy soils rich in nutrients, mainly in calcium. It produces dense clumps of flowers in May and June.

It is propagated from seed. Sow the seed at the beginning of April in a cold frame. It germinates after two to four weeks. When the seedlings are about 5 cm (2 in) tall plant them out in a sunny place 30 cm (12 in) apart in rows 45 cm (18 in) apart. They need frequent watering after planting, but will withstand drought if they are well rooted.

Collect the haulm before flowering. Cut off the herbaceous parts in May and either hang them up in small bundles to dry in the shade, or lay them out in thin layers and dry, without turning, at a temperature of up to 40 °C (104 °F). Store in well-sealed containers.

Garden Thyme relieves coughing, loosens phlegm, checks the reproduction of microbes and is disinfectant. It may be taken to treat persistent whooping cough, chronic bronchitis, bronchial asthma, chronic gastritis and spasms, as well as for digestive disorders, flatulence and diarrhoea. It may also be used as a gargle for disinfecting the mouth and throat, added to baths and applied on compresses on suppurating wounds.

Tea for influenza and illnesses where sweating is recommended: scald 10 g ($\frac{2}{5}$ oz) Thyme and 10 g ($\frac{2}{5}$ oz) Breckland Thyme in 250 ml (9 fl oz) water. Take the extract in two doses an hour before retiring.

Tilia cordata MILLER
Small-leaved Lime

Tiliaceae

● This tree with a broad ovoid crown grows to heights of 25−30 m (82−98 ft). The bark, at first smooth and brownish-grey, changes later into a brownish-grey to grey outer bark with shallow, lengthwise cracks. The shoots are usually bent, greenish-grey, often reddish on one side and glabrous. The two-year-old twigs are brown, the older ones greyish-brown. The alternate, oval, blunt buds are covered with olive-green to reddish-brown scales. The leaves are alternate, oval and toothed at the edges. The blade is bluish-green underneath, with bunches of rusty-brown hairs situated in the vein axils. The bisexual flowers grow in groups of five to seven in erect or slightly drooping dichasial cymes from a strap-shaped, membranous, glabrous bract. The buds are globular. The yellow-green calyx consists of five heart-shaped petals. There are five light yellow petals. A large number of stamens with orange-yellow anthers protrudes from the corolla. The pistil has a superior ovary, a column-shaped style and a club-shaped stigma. The ovary matures into oval, smooth, dark brown, fragile nuts (1).

● Small-leaved Lime is distributed on lowlands and uplands, growing mainly in damp woodland and hilly country, on screes or in oak woods. It is widely cultivated in villages and city parks as an ornamental and melliferous tree. It flowers in June.

Collect the whole inflorescence, together with the supporting bracts, in dry weather. Dry in thin layers in the shade, without turning. If you use artificial heat, the temperature should not exceed 40 °C (104 °F). It must not become damp after being dried, so store in well-sealed containers. Do not keep for longer than a year.

Decoction for disorders of the respiratory passages, influenza and colds: scald 10 g ($\frac{2}{3}$ oz) flowers with 250 ml (9 fl oz) boiling water, leave to infuse for 10 minutes, sweeten with honey and take warm before going to bed.

It strongly promotes sweating, stimulates bile production, has tranquillizing and diuretic properties, relieves spasms and facilitates expectoration. It is often used as a substitute for tea. Do not take Small-leaved Lime over a long period, because excessive sweating weakens the body. It is also said to have beneficial effects on the activity of the digestive system because it stimulates the formation of gastric juices, and on the heart, because it is said to increase the size of the coronary vessels. An extract made from the flowers may be taken internally to treat feverish illnesses, influenza, diseases of the respiratory passages, tonsillitis and heavy colds.

1

Trifolium pratense L.
Red Clover

Leguminosae

● This is a perennial herb. A rosette of long-stalked, basal, trimerous leaves grows from the tufted rhizome. The stems are simple or only slightly branched, erect, 20–50 cm (8–20 in) tall, jointed, somewhat angled and hairy. The stem leaves are alternate, the lower ones on long stalks with oval, tapering stipules, the upper ones short-stalked to almost sessile, mostly trimerous. Their leaflets are without stalks, oval, slightly indented at the tip, entire and hairy at the edges. They are green, almost glabrous above and sparsely covered with appressed hairs below. They have a diagonal whitish or reddish-brown blotch on the upper side. In the axils of the lateral and upper leaves, the stem bears one to four short-stalked or even sessile, globular to oval flower heads, which are partly covered with the stipules of the supporting leaves. Each flower head (1) contains 30–60 sessile bractless florets. The calyx is hairy, the corolla being red or rarely white. The fruit is a pod.

● Red Clover grows in meadows, in open woodland and in ditches, and is widely cultivated as animal fodder. It flowers from June to September. It is usually sown with the spring wheat, oats or barley. It produces basal leaves in the stubble, and flower-bearing stems in the following year. In favourable conditions, it can be left for two to three years. It thrives mainly in upland areas with higher humidity.

Collect the whole flower heads at the beginning of flowering, in sunny weather. Dry in the shade in thin layers at a temperature of up to 35 °C (95 °F). Less frequently, the whole haulm is used in popular healing. Collect it when the plant is in flower.

An extract made from the flower heads may be taken internally to treat bronchitis, hoarseness and to improve expectoration. A decoction made from the whole dried haulm may be taken internally for diarrhoea and other digestive disorders. It may be used as a mouth rinse to treat inflamed gums, and as a gargle for sore throats. It may be applied externally on compresses or for bathing various inflammatory skin ailments, as it disinfects the skin. It is used popularly as a flavour and fragrance-corrective in tea blends.

1

Tea for digestive troubles: scald 30 ml (2 tablespoons) dried flowers in 400 ml (14 fl oz) boiling water, cover and leave to stand for 10 minutes. Filter and take during the day in sips.

Trifolium repens L.
White Clover

Leguminosae

● This is a perennial herb 10–30 cm (4–12 in) in height. It has richly branched rhizomes forming a dense network. Creeping, often purplish rooting stems grow along the ground. They ascend at the ends and are sometimes covered with short hair. The alternate, trimerous leaves have stalks up to 20 cm (8 in) long with large basal, membranous stipules which are joined at the base and pointed with a small spine at the tip. The leaflets are without stalks, wedge-shaped oval, blunt-ended, finely toothed, and green with a diagonal white blotch, sometimes carmine-red. The globular flower heads grow from the leaf axils on stalks which are longer than the leaf stalks. These contain 40–80 florets (1) on stalks which are longer than the bracts. The florets droop downwards after fading. The bell-shaped, ten-veined calyx is divided into five tapering teeth, two long and three short. The symmetrical, white, greenish or pinkish corolla turns brown after fading. It contains 10 stamens, nine of which are joined with the filaments. The fruit is a pod which remains inside the dry calyx.

● White Clover grows in damp, manured meadows, damp woodland and riverside hedges, on river and stream deposits, along paths, in sports fields, on wasteland and other uncultivated ground, in fields among fodder crops and as a weed on lawns in gardens and parks. It flourishes on lowlands and uplands. It flowers from May to October. In gardens the decorative cultivar 'Atropurpurea' is grown. This has reddish-brown leaves, which are often tetra- or pentamerous. It flourishes mainly in sunny locations, such as on rockeries, slopes and entrenchments. The seeds are sown in April and germinate within one to two weeks.

Collect the flower heads before they fade, together with a short part of the stalk. Dry them in thin layers in the shade at a temperature of up to 35 °C (95 °F). Store in well-sealed containers.

White Clover may be taken internally to treat digestive disorders and persistent diarrhoea, bleeding, inflammation of the respiratory passages, rheumatism, gout and menstrual disorders. It may be applied externally as a skin disinfectant. The steam from the fresh decoction may be inhaled to relieve bronchitis.

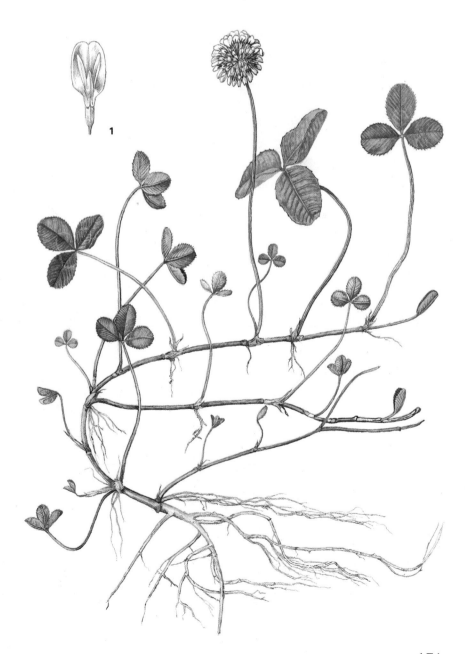

1

Tropaeolum majus L.
Nasturtium

Tropaeolaceae

VI–X ✳

V–X 🌿

VII–X 🐛

● This is an annual herb (perennial in frost-free conditions) with a stem up to 3 m (10 ft) long that may be climbing or may grow along the ground. The shrubby varieties are up to 30 cm (12 in) in height. The stem is fleshy, cylindrical and light green. In shrubby varieties, it is ascending and richly branched from the very base. The alternate, long-stalked leaves occasionally have twisting tendrils. The leaves are round and joined with the stalk roughly in the centre of the blade. Ten small veins run out in rays from the leaf stalk towards the edges of the shield-shaped leaf, where they terminate in a small spine. The leaves are entire and very shallowly lobed at the edges. The symmetrical, bisexual flowers grow singly on long stalks from the leaf axils. The yellow, orange, or often greenish calyx is composed of five sepals of unequal length, thus being two-lipped and protruding in a long, curved spur. The corolla is formed of five petals, of which the two upper ones are joined with the spur, the three lower ones having awl-shaped protuberances. They are yellow, orange or red and variegated. There are eight stamens arranged in two circles. The fruit (1) falls into three drupe-like capsules, each containing a single seed (2).

● Nasturtium is native to Peru and Chile in South America. It began to be cultivated in Europe in the 17th century, at first as an ornamental plant. It thrives in sunny positions, where up to 300 flowers can grow on a single plant. It flowers less in the semi-shade, although it produces abundant leaves. It flowers from June to the first frosts. Sow the seed directly in position in the middle of May. It germinates within two weeks. To speed up growth, it can be sown at the beginning of April in flower-pots, and the seedlings planted out at a distance of 30–40 cm (12–16 in) apart in the second half of May, when they are no longer threatened by frost. The creeping varieties may be sown either on top of walls, where they can trail downwards, or near supports up which they can climb.

Collect the flowers, the whole haulm or only the leaves and fruits, which provide the raw materials to the pharmaceutical industry. The flowers and leaves are usually used fresh, the fruits are dried in the sun. Sometimes the pericarps are removed first.

All parts of the plant contain constituents which act against disease-bearing bacteria, while having only a mild effect on normal intestinal bacteria. Nasturtium may, therefore, be more effective than antibiotics, particularly in treating acute and chronic infections of the urinary tract. These constituents also check infection in the respiratory system after influenza and so on. The daily dose of sap pressed from the fresh plants is 30–50 g (1–1 $\frac{3}{4}$ oz). Children may be given half the dose in milk in spoonfuls. The effects begin to show after two to three hours and last for 20 hours. The fruits are used for the same purposes as the haulm and the flowers.

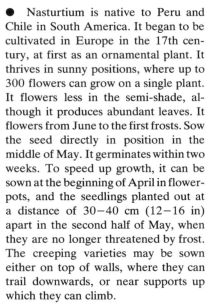

III–IV

 V–VI

Tussilago farfara L.
Coltsfoot

Compositae

● Coltsfoot is a perennial herb with a pulpy, creeping rhizome and long runners. Both flower and leaf buds grow on the rhizome. In early spring, unbranched, erect, web-like woolly stems, covered with reddish-brown, appressed scales, grow from the flower buds. They are terminated by a flower head with a single-rowed involucre, composed of 200–300 strap-shaped ray-florets and of 30–40 tubular disc-florets. The flowers are pale yellow. The flower heads close in rainy weather and in the evening. They droop downwards after fading. The receptacle is glabrous and non-paleaceous. The long-stalked basal leaves begin to sprout only when the flower heads start to fade. They have round, heart-shaped blades which are shallowly toothed at the edges and divided into 5–12 lobes. The blade is glossy and dark green above and greyish due to white felty hairs on the underside. When young, however, the leaves are densely white-felted on both sides. The fruits are long, cylindrical, glabrous achenes, with shiny white down at the tip.

● Coltsfoot grows on damp, clay soils in fields and meadows, along woodland pathways and in clearings, in ditches, on bare soil, in quarries, on dumping grounds and along railway embankments.

Collect the flowers with no more than 1 cm ($\frac{2}{5}$ in) of the stalk. Pick them shortly before they reach full bloom: fading flower heads would fall apart during drying. Dry them quickly by artificial heat, in thin layers. They must retain their original colour. Collect the leaves, together with the stalks, from the end of May until July. Do not collect any that have been attacked by rusts, which form orange spots on the underside of the blade. Dry them by artificial heat, placed side by side. They must not go black during drying. Do not squash the dried plants nor allow them to become damp. Store in well-sealed tins.

An extract from the flowers acts as an expectorant and may be taken internally to treat diseases of the respiratory passages, colds, hoarseness, coughs, influenza and asthma. It also contains anti-spasmodic constituents which speed up the healing of wounds, reduce inflammation and check the development and reproduction of microbes. A decoction made from the dried leaves may be applied externally on compresses on injured skin and small suppurating abscesses. Compresses made from the fresh leaves may be effective in relieving pain in the joints, rheumatism, gout, distorted joints and arthritic conditions. Place the washed leaves in two layers with the green upper side on the joint, hold in place with a bandage and wind a woollen scarf around.

173

Ulmus minor MILL.
Small-leaved Elm

III–IV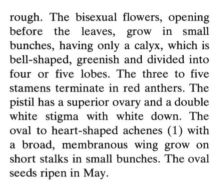

III–XI

Ulmaceae

● This tree grows to heights of up to 30 m (98 ft). The bark, brownish-grey when young, later changes into a blackish-grey, cracked outer bark which peels off in scales. The annual shoots are yellowish-green to brownish, and often crooked, the older twigs being light brown to ash-grey. The buds are alternate, arranged in two rows and of two types: the leaf buds are oval with pointed tips, the flower buds globular, both being covered with dark brown scales with fine hairs on the upper side. The leaves are alternate, oval, asymmetrical and doubly toothed. The blade is smooth on the upper side, rarely also rough. The bisexual flowers, opening before the leaves, grow in small bunches, having only a calyx, which is bell-shaped, greenish and divided into four or five lobes. The three to five stamens terminate in red anthers. The pistil has a superior ovary and a double white stigma with white down. The oval to heart-shaped achenes (1) with a broad, membranous wing grow on short stalks in small bunches. The oval seeds ripen in May.

● Small-leaved Elm grows in central and southern Europe in damp forests, on river and stream deposits and on screes, occurring up to altitudes of around 500 metres (1,600 ft) above sea level. In shallow soil it grows only as a shrub or small tree, producing numerous root suckers. It flowers in March. It used to be widely cultivated in parks and along city streets, but in recent decades it has suffered from Dutch Elm disease. It is propagated from seeds, which quickly lose their ability to germinate, so that the achenes need to be sown immediately after harvesting.

Collect the bark from small branches in March and April. Make two circular cuts 10–20 cm (4–8 in) apart, and join them with a lengthwise cut. Tap the bark with a blunt instrument and then peel it off whole. Dry in the sun or in a drying shed by artificial heat. Roots about 1 cm ($\frac{2}{5}$ in) thick or the bark from roots 2–3 cm ($\frac{3}{4}$–1 in) thick are also used in popular healing. Collect them from spring until late autumn from the root suckers, which grow out from the trunk to a distance of 20 cm (8 in). Dry in the same way as the bark.

Small-leaved Elm is astringent and may be used for treating diarrhoea and other digestive disorders. The freshly prepared decoction may be used for cleaning cuts. It is also recommended as a mouth wash for bleeding gums and oral infections, and as a gargle for sore throats. A decoction made from the bark may be used on compresses on inflamed skin, especially ulcers. Ointment can be made from powdered dried bark and lard.

1.

V–IX

 V–IX

IX–X

Urtica dioica L.
Common Nettle

Urticaceae

● Common Nettle is a perennial herb. The rhizome is richly branched, yellow, and spreads over large areas. Numerous erect stems up to 120 cm (47 in) in height grow from it. They are square, densely covered with long stinging hairs and short bristly little hairs. The simple stems branch out after being cut off. The leaves are opposite, stalked, oval to elongated, have long points and are either roundly indented or in a heart shape at the petiole, coarsely toothed at the edges and covered on both sides with stinging hairs. The yellowish, long, linear stipules at the stalk later fall. The flowers (1) are unisexual, the plants usually dioecious, although monoecious ones do occur. The flowers are arranged in drooping panicles and grow in groups of several from the leaf axils in the upper part of the stems. Only the male inflorescences are usually erect and shortly branched, having four perianth segments and four stamens. The female flowers have two perianth segments and a superior ovary with a stalkless stigma. The fruit is an achene. Nettles usually propagate vegetatively from the rhizomes.

● Common Nettle forms extensive growth in damp forests, occurring on lowlands and uplands. It is common around human settlements, where it grows in ditches, hedgerows, gardens, on rubbish dumps and other abandoned places. A form with more slender tapering leaves without the stinging hairs, or with only isolated hairs on the leaf stalks and main veins on the underside of the leaves, rarely occurs in forests. Common Nettle flowers from June to October.

Cut off the haulm of young, healthy plants (2) and dry as quickly as possible at a temperature of up to 60 °C (140 °F). It must not turn brown or black. Wear gloves to pull the foliage off the mown plants and dry the leaves in the same way as the haulm. The rhizomes can also be used. Wash them in water and dry quickly by artificial heat. Store in well-sealed containers.

The dried haulm and leaves have haemostatic and mild diuretic properties. They may also be used to treat diarrhoea and other digestive disorders. They contain substantial amounts of vitamins A and C. Anti-bacterial effects have also been discovered, so Common Nettle may also be effective in treating inflammatory diseases. It is believed to have beneficial effects on the formation of milk in nursing mothers. The rhizome, which is rich in calcium and tannins, is used mainly as an astringent.

> **Extract for use as a diuretic and to encourage milk production:** infuse 5 g ($\frac{1}{5}$ oz) dried leaves in 500 ml (18 fl oz) boiling water. Take during the day.
>
> **Decoction for hair care:** simmer 100 g ($3\frac{1}{2}$ oz) finely chopped haulm in a mixture of 500 ml (18 fl oz) vinegar and 500 ml (18 fl oz) water for 30 minutes. Rinse hair before going to bed.

Vaccinium myrtillus L.
Bilberry

V—VI

VII—VIII

Ericaceae

● Bilberry is a semi-shrub, 30—50 cm (12—20 in) in height, forming a dense network of horizontal roots and underground creeping runners. Erect, square, richly branched, small trunks grow from these. In the oldest parts they are round and covered in a thin, grey bark. The younger twigs are green, angled and erect. The deciduous leaves are alternate, short-stalked, and finely toothed at the edges. The blade is oval, either roundly indented or in a shallow heart shape at the base, light green, soft, glabrous, and later sometimes reddish to purplish. The drooping flowers (1) grow singly on stalks in the leaf axils. The calyx is inconspicuous, with four to five blunt small teeth. The light green, pinkish corolla is globosely dome-shaped with four to five small, short teeth at the tip. Inside the corolla there are eight to ten stamens arranged in two circles, with the stigma protruding from them. The inferior ovary has four to five cells and matures into globular berries which are notched at the top with the remains of the calyx and the filamentous stigma. The berries are blackish-blue with a greyish bloom and have blue, juicy pulp.

● Bilberry grows on acid, humous soil in woods on lowlands and in mountains, where it thrives on stony slopes and rocks above the upper tree line.

Pick the young leaves, mainly from the non-flowering twigs. Remove any damaged leaves and dry the healthy ones as quickly as possible in a thin layer in the shade at a temperature of up to 40 °C (104 °F). They must retain their fresh green colour. Collect the fruits when they are fully ripe and leave them to shrivel in the sun. Complete the drying process by artificial heat. They should not become completely hard. Since the dried plant absorbs moisture from the air, it is necessary to dry it out again from time to time.

A decoction made from the leaves may be taken internally to treat diarrhoea, bleeding and diabetes. It has diuretic action and is also anti-bacterial. It may be used as a mouth wash or gargle to treat bleeding gums, oral infections and sore throats. The fruits may be used in doses of 10 g ($\frac{2}{5}$ oz) for treating diarrhoea, either dry or crushed in water. The juice from the fresh fruits is an excellent preparation for regeneration of the mucous membranes. The blue colour of the fruits penetrates diseased mucous membranes, forming a thin layer with its endothel, under which a new, healthy endothel forms. The upper, blackish-blue layer then falls off. The fresh juice has mild laxative properties, in contrast with the dry fruits.

1

Compote from the fresh fruits: sterilize in their own juice for 20 minutes at 80 °C (176 °F).

Vaccinium vitis-idaea L.
Cowberry

Ericaceae

● Cowberry is a sub-shrub 10−30 cm (4−12 in) high with a creeping, branched, scaly rhizome. Rounded arched to erect twigs which are downy when young grow from it. The leaves (1) are alternate, short-stalked, oval, either indented or round at the tip, thick and leathery, entire or finely toothed and slightly inrolled at the edges, narrowing abruptly towards the stalk. They do not fall in the autumn. The blade is glossy and dark green on the upper side, and paler with brown dots on the underside. The flowers (2) grow grouped in racemes at the branch tips, the tip of the racemes drooping downwards. The calyx is bell-shaped, and divided into five lobes. The white to light pink, slightly fragrant corolla is spherically dome-shaped and divided at the top only into four to five tips. There are 10 stamens with tubular protuberances in groups of two on the orange-yellow anthers. The inferior ovary has a long, straight style at the tip, which protrudes from the corolla. It matures into a globular, juicy, floury, slightly acid berry (3), which remains white for a long time, later partly turning red, being completely red and glossy only when fully ripe. It contains small brown seeds (4).

● Cowberry grows in acid, non-calcareous soils in dry pinewoods, peat-bogs, poor sandy soils and in rocky upland meadows. It flowers in May and June.

Collect the leaves by pulling them off the non-flowering twigs. Remove any damaged leaves and dry the healthy ones as quickly as possible in the shade at a temperature of up to 40 °C (104 °F). They should retain their original colour. A decoction is used for treating diarrhoea, inflammatory kidney and urinary disorders, kidney stones, diabetes and haemorrhaging. Cowberry also has diuretic and anti-

bacterial properties. The daily dose is a decoction made from 10 g ($\frac{2}{3}$ oz) of the dried leaves.

The fruits are also used in popular medicine. They are rich in vitamin C and contain constituents with similar properties to those of the foliage, although in smaller quantities. Apart from this, they also stimulate digestion and increase the appetite. Collect them at the end of September and in October (earlier in

lower positions). The juice from the fruits reduces fevers, for example, in influenza and other infectious diseases. The fresh fruits may be processed into compotes, jams, jellies, syrups or wine. To avoid destroying the vitamin C content, do not allow the fruits to come into contact with metal. Cooking times should be kept to a minimum. The fruits are not recommended for people with kidney stones.

Compote: mix 1 kg (2 lb 3 oz) fruits with 100−200 g (3 $\frac{1}{2}$ −7 oz) sugar, heat and boil for a short time. Pour into glass containers and sterilize.

Valeriana officinalis L.
Common Valerian

Valerianaceae

Valerian is a perennial herb growing to a height of 30–150 cm (12–59 in). The rhizome (1) is short and thick, with lateral runners from which numerous branched roots grow. The rhizome produces a rosette of basal odd-pinnate, stalked leaves (3) with a winged central spindle. These are composed of tapering, sparsely and coarsely toothed leaflets, the terminating leaflet being larger than the lateral ones, of which there are 6–11 pairs. The stems are erect, cylindrical, furrowed, simple, and bear several pairs of leaves. The stem leaves are opposite, the lower ones being stalked, the upper ones sessile and less divided than the basal ones. The stem terminates in a rich cyme of bisexual, asymmetrical flowers (2), divided into three branches. During flowering, the calyx is inconspicuously five-toothed with a light pink, or more rarely white, funnel-shaped corolla divided into five tips of unequal length. There are three stamens. The pistil has an inferior ovary divided into three cells, the seed, however, developing in only one of them. The fruit is an achene enveloped in the dried calyx. It is round at the base and pointed at the tip, flattened on one side and with white down.

Common Valerian grows on lowlands and uplands in damp meadows, ditches, river side hedges, woods and on overgrown rocks. Collecting the rhizomes from wild plants would destroy a significant number and harm the ecology. Therefore, for pharmaceutical purposes, these are obtained from cultivated plants. It is grown in light to medium heavy, sufficiently damp, neutral or alkaline soils. Sow the seed immediately after it matures at the end of summer or in early spring in March and April. Thin out the seedlings to 30–40 cm (12–16 in) apart. It can also be propagated vegetatively by dividing the older clumps after harvesting in autumn.

Dig up the rhizomes and roots from two-year-old plants in October and November. Clean thoroughly and dry in the shade at a temperature of up to 30 °C (86 °F). Dry the haulm in small bundles in the shade in natural heat.

Both extracts and decoctions may be prepared from the rhizome. These act as tranquillizers in the case of nervous disorders, heart neuroses, insomnia, migraine and so on. Alcohol extracts may be effective against spasms in smooth muscle. A tranquillizing tea may be prepared from the haulm. Valerian should not be used for prolonged periods because it causes agitation; it is not advisable to use it in home medicines. It forms part of many tea blends, for treating heart, nerve and gastric disorders.

Veratrum lobelianum BERNH.
Hellebore

Liliaceae

● Hellebore is a greenish-yellow perennial herb growing to heights of 60–150 cm (24–59 in). It has a perpendicular rhizome, which is either cylindrical or conical, non-articulate, simple or multi-headed, greyish-brown to black on the surface and whitish inside, with remnants of old, dry leaves at the top. Yellowish wrinkled roots grow from the rhizome. Every year, broadly oval leaves, up to 30 cm (12 in) long and 12 cm (5 in) wide with prominent, parallel veins, along which the leaves are markedly gathered, as if pleated, also grow from the rhizome. The blade tapers towards both ends, is glabrous on the upper side and downy to felted on the underside. The leaf sheaths form a pseudo-stalk. The flower-bearing stems appear only when the plant is 10–30 years old. Even then, the plants do not flower every year, but only after five to ten years. The stem is thick, erect, leafy, branched at the top and covered with dense, soft hair. The stem leaves are alternate and tapering, transforming into bracts in the inflorescences. The flowers form rich panicles of dense racemes. The perianth is white, greenish or yellowish. The fruit is a capsule.

● Hellebore grows in damp meadows in the mountains, and at springs. Plants washed down from higher elevations very occasionally occur in meadows, in river side thickets and near running water in lower regions. It flowers from June to August, and is cultivated as an ornamental plant in gardens.

It is propagated by the division of clumps growing from multi-headed rhizomes: cultivation from seed is time-consuming and the seeds germinate irregularly. The plant requires a damp location with a humus-rich soil or peat. All parts of the plant are poisonous.

The rhizomes from three- to four-year-old plants are collected in September and October by the pharmaceutical industry. The rhizomes are washed, halved lengthwise and dried as quickly as possible.

Hellebore contains substances which lower blood pressure, dilate the blood vessels and slow down the pulse and respiration rates. Hypotensive medi-

cines are manufactured from it. It is also used in veterinary medicines as a reviving and diuretic preparation and for treating digestive disorders. It acts as an insect repellent. The powder from the dried rhizome causes violent sneezing, pain in the eyes and tear ducts, burning in the mouth and on the skin followed by

a numbing sensation. If the plant is ingested, the symptoms of poisoning are vomiting, painful or even bloody diarrhoea, dilation of the pupils and slowing down or even stopping of breathing and the heart. Hellebore is poisonous and should never be used in home medicines.

Verbascum thapsus L.
Torchwort

VII–IX ◉

V–X ✦

Scrophulariaceae

This is a biennial herb up to 200 cm (79 in) in height. A basal rosette of leaves grows from the spindle-shaped taproot in the first year. These are oval, narrowing into a short petiole, finely toothed at the edges, round at the tip and densely felty. The basal rosette overwinters, and the following year an erect, simple or sparsely branched stem with yellowish-white felt grows from it. The stem leaves are alternate, elongated to tapering, pointed at the tip and without stalks. Each leaf extends along the stem as far as the leaf below it. The stems and the erect branches terminate in a long spike of flowers growing in small bunches of two to seven on short stalks, from the axils of oval, tapering bracts. The flowers are bisexual and regular. The calyx is hairy and divided into five pointed tips which enclose the bud when young. The light yellow wheel-shaped corolla is composed of five round petals. There are five stamens, two of which have long, glabrous filaments and three have short, white woolly filaments. The fruit is a double-celled, brown capsule (1) with seeds (2).

Torchwort grows on rocky slopes, in pastures, in clearings and quarries, on old walls, road and railway embankments, stony river embankments, on waste ground, dumping grounds and other uncultivated ground. It grows on lowlands and uplands. It flowers from July to September and is very easy to cultivate from seed. It flourishes on poor sandy or gravelly soils with sufficient calcium content.

Collect the corollas, with their accrete stamens, just as they are opening in dry weather, ideally in the morning. Do not squash them. Dry them quickly in thin layers at a temperature of 50−60 °C (122−140 °F). They should retain their bright yellow colour and honey-like fragrance. Store in air-tight containers. The stem leaves from two-year-old plants may also be collected. Dry them in the shade in thin layers, without turning, at a temperature of up to 40 °C (104 °F). They should still have their original greyish-green colour when dry.

The active constituents of Torchwort facilitate expectoration, relieve irritating coughs and help to relieve inflammation in the mouth and throat. They also help relieve spasms. It may be taken either as an extract made with boiling water or as a decoction. A decoction made from the leaves may be taken internally for treating diarrhoea or applied externally on inflamed skin.

Extract for improving expectoration: pour 500 ml (18 fl oz) boiling water or milk over 5 g ($\frac{1}{5}$ oz) dried plant and leave to macerate for 10 minutes.

Verbena officinalis L.
Vervain

Verbenaceae

● Vervain is a perennial plant 20–70 cm (8–28 in) in height. It has a slender, not particularly deeply penetrating, branched root from which grows a rigidly erect, square stem. This is branched at the top and depressed into furrows on two sides, rough at the edges, turning woody in the lower part, and glabrous. The opposite leaves, which are smaller in the lower part, elongated, coarsely toothed to lobed and pinnate-indented at the edges, taper into a short petiole. The central leaves are larger and divided into three sections, of which the central one is the largest, and lobed. The lateral ones are longish linear and toothed at the edge. The upper leaves are without stalks, longish, tapering, toothed or almost entire. All the leaves are tough, greyish-green, covered with short, spreading hair and rough with coarse hair. The flowers (1) are without stalks in long terminal or lateral spikes in the axils of small bracts. The calyx is tubular, glandular and divided into four to five teeth. The corolla is faintly two-lipped, and coloured light violet or white. The fruits are cylindrical nutlets.

● Vervain grows in pastures, on river and stream banks, along paths and fences, on dumping grounds and other abandoned places, thriving mainly in low-lying warm positions. It flowers from July to September.

Collect the flowering haulm. The root, too, may be collected. Cut off the tops of the stems before the fruits ripen and dry in the shade at a temperature of up to 40 °C (104 °F). An extract or decoction may be taken internally to improve the appetite, and to stimulate production of gastric juices and the metabolism. It has a somewhat astringent effect. It is recommended for insomnia, migraine and nervous disorders. It has diuretic properties and stimulates bile production, so it may be taken to treat diseases of the urinary system and gallbladder. It promotes expectoration and is widely used for inflammatory ailments of the respiratory system. It is taken to treat digestive disorders, diarrhoea, gastric pain, liver diseases and enlarged spleen. In popular healing, it is also used for treating asthma, sore throats and feverish illnesses. The decoction may be used as a gargle for sore throats or bleeding gums. Compresses may also be prepared from the decoction for inflamed skin.

1

Extract for use cold as a gargle: macerate 15 ml (1 tablespoon) dried haulm in 400 ml (14 fl oz) water.

Extract for treating diarrhoea: macerate 2.5 g ($\frac{1}{10}$ oz) dried haulm in 200 ml (7 fl oz) boiling water for 15 minutes. Take in several doses three to four times daily.

181

Veronica officinalis L.
Heath Speedwell

Scrophulariaceae

● Heath Speedwell is a perennial, low herb with stems that grow along the ground, are up to 60 cm (24 in) long and covered with short hairs. The creeping parts of the stem take root and the flower-bearing, rounded parts are ascending in the period of flowering. The opposite, short-stalked, oval leaves taper in a wedge shape towards the stalk. They are entire at the stalk, otherwise they are finely toothed, round or blunt-pointed at the ends and with scattered hair. From the leaf axils in the upper part of the stem grow erect, at first compact and later elongating racemes of flowers. The flowers are borne on short stalks in the axils of tapering bracts. The calyx is formed of four tapering lobes of equal length. The bell-shaped, rotate, light bluish-violet or white, symmetrical corolla (1), composed of four petals of unequal size, which are fused at the base in the very short tube, soon falls. Two stamens with bluish-violet anthers are joined with the corolla. The superior ovary with its long style and flat stigma matures into a flat, indented, glandular-hairy capsule.

● Heath Speedwell grows in open forests and clearings, woodland meadows and dry pastures, along woodland pathways and in hedgerows. It is distributed on lowlands and uplands. It flowers from June to August. It is easy to cultivate, thriving in semi-shade in non-calcareous soil. It can be propagated either from seed or vegetatively from the rooting stems.

Collect the flowering haulm from June to August. Cut off the lower part where there are still fresh leaves with a knife or scissors. Dry as quickly as possible in thin layers in the shade at a temperature of up to 35 °C (95 °F). Do not turn the haulm during drying, because the corollas fall easily. It must retain its original colour. Store in well-sealed containers.

Heath Speedwell was highly valued in the past and is used in popular healing to this day. It promotes the dispersal of phlegm. A decoction made from the haulm may be taken internally for better expectoration. It is also used as an auxiliary preparation for treating diseases of the urinary tract and is thought to be effective in treating rheumatism, as a diuretic and for certain skin conditions (eczema, burns). It is often combined in tea blends with other herbs with similar effects.

Tea for expectoration: scald 2.5 ml ($\frac{1}{2}$ teaspoon) dried haulm with 500 ml (18 fl oz) boiling water. Infuse for 10 minutes and take the warm drink during the day in sips.

Gargle: boil 10 g ($\frac{2}{5}$ oz) Speedwell haulm, 10 g ($\frac{2}{5}$ oz) Sage and 5 g ($\frac{1}{5}$ oz) Chamomile in 500 ml (18 fl oz) water for two minutes.

Viburnum lantana L.
Common Viburnum

Caprifoliaceae

● This shrub is 1–4 metres (3–13 ft) high, richly branched with erect branches. The annual shoots are grey-felted (4) and the older twigs yellowish-brown. The erect, white-felted buds are scaleless. The flower buds are squat and conical in shape, growing at the ends of the shoots. The leaf buds are club-shaped and ridged. The leaves are opposite, oval, have short points and are toothed at the edges. The blade is greyish-green felty on the underside, and has prominent veins. The bisexual, regular flowers, arranged in panicle-like cymes, grow on greyish-green felty stalks in the axils of small, awl-shaped bracts. The calyx is small, green and five-toothed. The corolla is bell-like and funnel-shaped, dingy white, and divided into five oval lobes which are round at the tip (1). The five stamens have white filaments and yellow anthers. The small buds are pinkish. The fruits mature into oval, flattened drupes, which are green when young (5), and black and glossy when fully ripe (2). They contain a flat, brownish small stone (3).

● Common Viburnum is distributed in warm regions of western, central and southern Europe, growing mainly on rocky or stony slopes, particularly south-facing ones, and in open woodland, mostly in calcium-rich soils. It is often planted in parks as an ornamental shrub. It may be propagated from seed or from root suckers. The basal branches covered with soil take root.

Collect the leaves and bark. Dry them in natural heat in the shade and store in well-sealed containers. The fruits are poisonous.

Common Viburnum is used only in popular healing, although less than it used to be. The ripe fruits were used in the past, not without risk, as a laxative. A decoction was taken for pain in the digestive tract. As the fruits are poisonous, they should never be used in home medicines. A decoction made from the inflorescences used to be added to baths to relieve paralysed limbs. A decoction made from the leaves may soothe oral infections and sore throats. In popular healing in Romania, a decoction is prepared from the leaves and young sprigs to put on compresses on swellings, sprained ankles, corns, abscesses and ulcers on the legs. The bark is thought to be an effective haemostatic, and a decoction sometimes taken internally to treat menstrual troubles and bleeding diarrhoea, and used as a mouth wash or gargle, to treat bleeding gums and to firm up the gums.

Viburnum opulus L.
Guelder Rose, Snowball Tree

Caprifoliaceae

● This shrub or small tree grows to heights of 2–4 metres (7–13 ft). The bark is light brown and the annual shoots erect, yellowish or reddish-brown and bluntly angled. Older twigs are ash-grey and six-sided. The opposite, oval, pointed, short-stalked buds are covered with two joined, greenish-brown or red enveloping scales. The terminal buds occur most often in pairs. From the buds grow opposite, broadly oval, tri- to pentamerous leaves which are coarsely toothed at the edges and have pointed lobes. The petiole, depressed into a furrow, has several round, red glands on short stalks near the blade. The flowers are arranged in terminal, richly branched, flat or globular cymes. These are of two types; larger, white, flat sterile ones on the periphery and smaller, white or reddish bisexual ones in the centre. The calyx is short and tubular with three to five teeth, the corolla globular with five points. There are five stamens. The inferior ovary matures into a red drupe (1) with a single stone.

● It is distributed throughout the whole of Europe, extending northwards as far as the polar forest border, growing in damp to wet places in deciduous forests, riverside hedgerows and at springs on lowlands and uplands. Varieties with either only sterile flowers in spherical inflorescences or variegated and golden-yellow leaves bearing yellow or golden-yellow fruits are cultivated in gardens and parks. A variety with sweetish fruits also exists. Guelder Rose flowers from May to July. It is propagated either from root runners or cuttings from the lower branches that take root when covered with earth. When propagating from seed, soak the fruits in water for 24 hours in order to remove the pulp, which slows down germination. They germinate after quite a long time and irregularly.

Collect the bark in early spring or in autumn, and the ripe fruits when they mature at the end of September or in October. They persist on the branches long into the winter. Extracts are manufactured commercially from the fresh bark and fruits. These have astringent and anti-spasmodic properties. They are used predominantly in gynaecology, especially during pregnancy when there is a danger of miscarriage, as they reduce contractions of the uterine muscle. The Polish pharmacopoeia recommends a spirit extract for treating painful menstruation, uterine spasms, haemorrhaging during the menopause and a tendency towards premature delivery or miscarriage. The plant is poisonous and should never be used in home medicines. Vomiting and diarrhoea occur when the permitted doses are exceeded, or in the case of long-term use.

1

Vinca minor L.
Lesser Periwinkle

Apocynaceae

● The Lesser Periwinkle is a perennial, low semi-shrub only 15—20 cm (6—8 in) in height. It has a long, creeping, richly branched, slender, brown rhizome which grows out over large areas. A large number of runners grow from it. They are either creeping, rooting and sterile or ascending, turning woody at the base, rotund and flower-bearing. The evergreen, leathery leaves are opposite, short-stalked, tapering to oval and blunt-pointed. They taper into a wedge shape towards the stalk. On the upper side, they are dark green and glossy, on the underside lighter and glabrous. They have an entire, slightly inrolled edge. The bisexual, regular flowers grow singly in the leaf axils on long stalks. The glabrous calyx is divided into four to five narrowly tapering lobes. The corolla is fused into a narrow tube at the base, and divided into five broadly wedge-shaped to oval petals. These are spirally coiled before opening, later flat and spreading, light blue or bluish-violet, less frequently reddish-violet or white. The superior ovary matures into two slender follicles.

● Lesser Periwinkle grows in open oak woods and hedges, on overgrown rocks, and sometimes even on old walls and ruins. It is often cultivated in gardens and cemeteries. The flowers open in April and May, occasionally again in the autumn. Sometimes a whole cover of shrubs never flowers at all and the plants propagate only vegetatively. Double-flowered forms or ones with leaves with white or yellow blotches are cultivated in gardens. It is easy to propagate vegetatively from the rooting runners or by dividing the extensive dense growth into small clumps. It can also be cultivated from seed. Wild plants are protected in some countries.

Collect the whole flowering and non-flowering shoots. Cut them off with scissors and dry as quickly as possible in the shade at a temperature of up to 45 °C (113 °F).

It has diuretic and astringent properties and is used in popular medicine for treating diarrhoea, all forms of haemorrhaging, bronchial catarrh, for stimulating digestion and as a general tonic. It may be applied to inflamed mucous membranes in the mouth. Lesser Periwinkle can be dangerous and should never be used in home medicines.

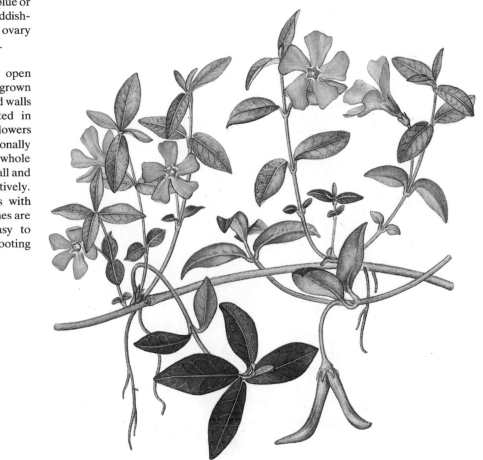

Viola odorata L.
Sweet Violet

Violaceae

III, X

III–IV

IV–V

This is a perennial, fragrant herb with stems up to 15 cm (6 in) in height. The cylindrical, richly branched rhizome produces numerous runners with fine, branched roots. Rosettes of basal leaves, which are furled into a cornet shape when young, grow from the rhizome. They have a long stalk and a roundish kidney-shaped or broadly heart-shaped blade which is finely and densely toothed at the edge. On the stalk under the blade there are two broadly oval, pointed stipules, which are either entire or fringed with glands in the upper part. The leaves are covered with fine hair. Single flowers grow from the axils of the basal leaf stalks on square stalks which bend downwards into a hook at the ends. Approximately in the middle of the flower stalk there are two opposite, tapering bracts. The calyx is composed of five oval sepals of equal size, which are fused at the base and have spreading appendices. Four of the petals are oval, the fifth is extended in the centre into a tubular spur. They are most frequently bluish-violet, sometimes purplish-red, white or cream-yellow. The fruit is a capsule containng brown seeds.

Sweet Violet is common in woods and hedges but somewhat rarer in the north and west of Britain. It flowers in March and April, these flowers being, as a rule, sterile. In May, inconspicuous, green stunted flowers (1) grow near the ground; they are self-fertilizing and most of the fruits develop from them.

Collect the rhizome, together with the root hairs, either in early spring or in autumn. Rinse in water and dry in the shade at a temperature of up to 35 °C (95 °F). Store in well-sealed containers. The flowers from the violet-flowering plants only may also be collected for medicinal purposes. Pick them together with a part of their stalk. Remove the calyx and dry in a thin layer in the shade. It is important to retain both the original colour and the fragrance. Store in well-sealed containers which cannot be penetrated by light. The leaves may be collected in April and May and dried in the shade.

The active constituents promote mucus excretion, facilitate expectoration and stimulate urine production. An expectorant tea may be prepared from the rhizome, the dried or even the fresh leaves. Boil these for two minutes and take 200 ml (7 fl oz) three times a day.

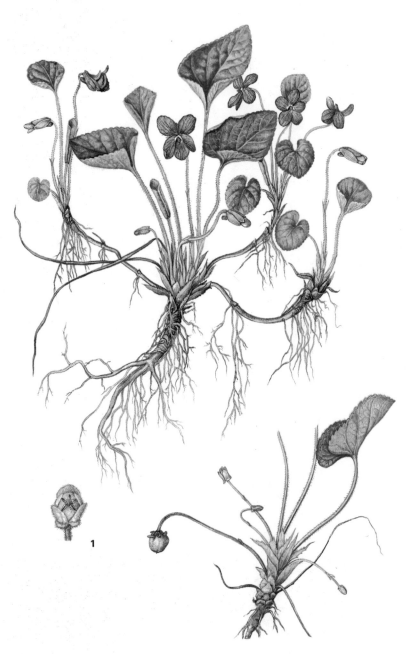

1

Decoction for compresses on inflamed swellings: boil 20 g ($\frac{3}{4}$ oz) leaves in 125 ml (4 $\frac{1}{2}$ fl oz) vinegar for two minutes.

Extract for treating headaches and sore throats: scald 15 g ($\frac{1}{2}$ oz) flowers with 250 ml (9 fl oz) water and macerate for 10 minutes. Take three times daily.

Viola tricolor L.
Wild Pansy, Heartsease

Violaceae

● This annual or biennial herb grows 10–20 cm (4–8 in) tall. A semi-creeping or ascending stem, usually richly branched, glabrous or with scattered hair, angled, pulpy and articulate, grows from a spindle-shaped, simple root. The stalked leaves are alternate and have large stipules, which are deeply lobed and have an oval terminating section. The lower ones are almost round, the upper ones oval, and coarsely to sparsely toothed at the edges. The bisexual, symmetrical flowers grow individually from the leaf axils on long stalks which bend into a hook at the top with a small stipule. There are five sepals, which are tapering, pointed, either longer than or the same length as the corolla, and have a round to oval appendix at the base. The corolla is a light yellow. The upper petal and spur are usually purplish, the spur being about the same length as the calyx appendices. There are five stamens with short filaments, two bearing a long appendix. The superior ovary matures into an oval capsule with light brown seeds.

● Wild Pansy grows on dumping grounds, waste land and on disturbed sandy soils throughout Britain. It also grows as a weed in gardens and fields. It flowers from April to October. It is widely cultivated as a medicinal plant for the pharmaceutical industry. Wild Pansy and Clover seeds are sown together with oats or spring barley. The plants are picked out of the stubble after the cereal crops have been harvested. The roots are then removed and the whole haulm dried in thin layers in the shade, without turning, at a temperature of up to 50 °C (122 °F). The leaves and flowers must retain the original colours. The flowers may be collected from plants growing wild. Dry on sheets of paper to catch the seed for the next sowing. Wild Pansy may also be cultivated on its own. Sow the seeds at the end of May in shallow rows 25–30 cm (10–12 in) apart and roll lightly. They germinate in the light within three to four weeks. Harvesting can be done mechanically.

Wild Pansy has diuretic properties, facilitates expectoration, assists in the elimination of harmful substances from the body and has reviving effects. It increases the firmness of fine blood vessels, stimulates the oxygenation of the blood, checks the excretion of iodine and increases the calcium content of the blood and bones. In popular healing, an extract may be taken internally to treat diseases of the respiratory passages, whooping cough, lung complaints and catarrh. A decoction can be used for rinsing skin rashes, particularly in children.

Viscum laxum BOISS. et REUT.
Mistletoe

Loranthaceae

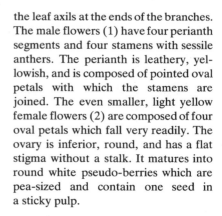

☠ ● This is a semi-parasitic, evergreen small shrub up to 60 cm (24 in) in height, growing on trees, and over-wintering. The trunk and branches fork regularly. The bark on the young twigs is olive-green or yellowish-green, glabrous and glossy, on the older twigs greenish-grey to grey. The leaves are opposite, leathery and tough, without stalks, elongatedly oval, yellowish-green, blunt-ended, tapering into a wedge shape at the base, and are entire with parallel veins. The plant is dioecious. The inconspicuous unisexual flowers are without stalks in groups of three to five in the branch forks and in the leaf axils at the ends of the branches. The male flowers (1) have four perianth segments and four stamens with sessile anthers. The perianth is leathery, yellowish, and is composed of pointed oval petals with which the stamens are joined. The even smaller, light yellow female flowers (2) are composed of four oval petals which fall very readily. The ovary is inferior, round, and has a flat stigma without a stalk. It matures into round white pseudo-berries which are pea-sized and contain one seed in a sticky pulp.

● Mistletoe lives parasitically, mainly on poplars and apple trees. Plants with broad leaves, which grow on firs, are known as the subspecies *abietis*, and those on deciduous trees as the separate species *Viscum album*. These are not distinguished for pharmaceutical purposes. Mistletoe flowers in March and April. The fruits ripen in November and December. The plant can also be cultivated, the seeds being stuck on to the branches or trunks of appropriate trees. A significant number of seeds, however, are destroyed by tits and mice.

The younger twigs, together with the leaves, very occasionally also with the fruits, are used for medicinal purposes. These are collected in winter from felled trees. They are dried, hung up in small bundles, at a temperature of up to 40 °C (104 °F). The fresh plants may also be used.

Hypotensive preparations as well as medicines for treating hardening of the arteries are manufactured commercially. Mistletoe also contains constituents which check the growth of tumours, affect heart activity, and have haemostatic and anthelmintic effects. It was used in the past in popular healing for treating epilepsy and various spasms. Mistletoe is poisonous and should never be used in home medicines. It is currently the subject of pharmaceutical research.

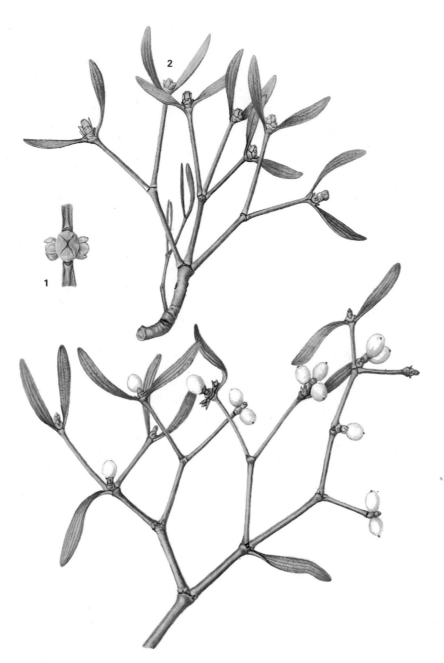

Index
of Latin names

Index
of common names